No Golden Cities

No Golden Cities

Thelma C. Nason

ILLUSTRATIONS BY PAUL WILLIAMS

CROWELL-COLLIER PRESS, NEW YORK, NEW YORK
COLLIER-MACMILLAN LIMITED, LONDON

For Marshall who knows
and loves the Southwest.

Library of Congress Catalog Card Number: 70–130022

The Macmillan Company
866 Third Avenue
New York, New York 10022

Collier-Macmillan Canada Ltd., Toronto, Ontario

Printed in the United States of America

1   2   3   4   5   6   7   8   9   10

CONTENTS

OFF TO FOUND A
NEW COLONY

A cold, winter sun glittered over northern Mexico one January day in 1598. Don Juan de Oñate, sitting erect on his horse on a low hill, held himself stiff to keep from shivering in the sharp wind. In spite of his thick cloak, the steel armor he wore seemed to clamp the chill against his body. The boy on the black horse beside him could not prevent a shiver now and then. But he did not complain. Like his father, he held his head high and watched the camp in the valley below.·

The scene boiled with activity, like an anthill that has been disturbed. Figures made small by distance scurried here and there. Toy horses pranced. On the outskirts, dust clouds stained the sunlight as other figures rounded up cows, goats, sheep, and oxen. Then, as if by magic, the hurrying figures began to sort themselves out. The horsemen gathered at one end of the camp. Behind them came a group of brown-robed priests. Wagons and carts, some of them with wheels six feet high, began to form in line. The animals made a long tail at the end of the procession which began to move slowly forward.

The thin, stern face of Don Juan relaxed in lines of pride and relief. At last his expedition was on the way. At last he was going to found a Spanish colony in the territory of New Mexico!

The boy, Cristóbal, watched his father's face. He knew how long Don Juan had waited for this moment. In 1595 he made an agreement with the viceroy of New Spain, as Mexico was then called, to establish the first settlement in the territory to the north. Very soon after the contract was made, another viceroy was sent to the country. This new representative of the king was a careful and cautious man. He wanted to make sure that Don Juan was the best choice for this important undertaking. While he studied the matter, the enemies of Don Juan began to work against him. Rumors that he was not a fit leader even reached across the ocean. The king and his advisers on New World affairs, the Council of the Indies, began to wonder. At one point, they even chose a new leader for the expedition.

Don Juan, however, believed in himself and his plans. He went ahead recruiting men for his army. He spent a fortune on provisions and supplies, with

wagons and carts to carry them. He gathered his soldiers, many of them with their wives and children, in northern Mexico. There they waited for permission to set forth. Month after weary month they waited. Some became discouraged and left the camp. Provisions were used up and had to be replaced at great cost. At last, the king gave permission to go ahead. Now, on January 26, 1598, they were finally on their way!

Don Juan and Cristóbal rode down the hill and took their places in the procession. As general of the army and governor of the colony, Don Juan rode at the head of the column. With him was Juan de Zaldívar, the field commander. Cristóbal joined the captains who rode with Vicente de Zaldívar, the third-ranking officer. These brown-bearded young Zaldívar brothers were Don Juan's nephews, Cristóbal's cousins.

Cristóbal had a right to ride with the officers. Though he was only twelve, he had been a lieutenant in his father's army for two years. One meaning for the word "lieutenant" is assistant or helper, and we may be sure that Cristóbal helped his father in many ways. Don Juan was training his son for the life of a soldier. Perhaps this was the life for which he was best suited. On his mother's side, the boy was the great-grandson of Cortés, the conqueror of Mexico, and the great-great-grandson of Montezuma, the last Indian ruler of that country. Thus the blood of the Aztec kings was mixed in his veins with the blood of the Spanish conquerors of the New World.

In spite of the long delay he had caused, the king of Spain was eager for a colony to be established in New Mexico. He had three reasons for his interest. In the first place, there were tales of great wealth in the north. Everyone had heard of the Seven Cities of Cíbola, where the doors were said to be studded with turquoises and whole streets of goldsmiths were needed to work the gold of the region. People believed these stories. They still remembered the fabulous treasure taken from the Aztecs of Mexico and the Incas of Peru. It seemed reasonable that still more wealth might be found.

Another reason was the strong desire of the Spanish kings to spread the Christian religion. Missionary priests were sent with every exploring party to teach Christianity to the natives. Spanish leaders were instructed to help in every way possible. This work was always mentioned by the rulers as the main purpose of new explorations.

The third reason came from the fact that people in the Old World knew very little about the geography of North America. Most people believed that, somewhere to the north, a strip of water called the Strait of Anián united the Atlantic and Pacific oceans. Since they also believed North America to be much smaller than it is, they thought that the land north of Mexico must lie near Anián. King Philip hoped that one of his men might discover the strait and hold it for Spain.

So a colony was to be settled in "the new Mexico." Among the colonists and soldiers were many wealthy people who brought their servants and fine clothes with them. They had put their money into this expedition because they believed they would become even richer in the new land. But rich or poor, gentlemen or adventurers, all the colonists expected a golden reward for the hardships they would face.

As the train proceeded, some of the horsemen rode far ahead as scouts. The rest traveled with the caravan to protect it in case of danger. A few women of the train rode horseback on sidesaddles. Others journeyed with the children in the loaded carts, many of which were covered as a protection against sun and wind. These carts were the noisiest part of the procession. The solid wooden wheels, turning on wooden axles, began to squeak and creak as soon as they started. The noise grew louder and louder until the constant screeching made the eardrums ache. Behind the carts, the seven thousand animals stretched for a long distance across the Mexican hills.

On the fourth day, the expedition reached the Conchos River, which was swollen by winter rains. Dark water swirled between steep banks. The field commander sent riders up and down the river searching for a ford. They found one place where the banks were less steep. But even there, the soldiers looked down on the foaming, chocolate-colored water and shook their heads.

General de Oñate galloped to the spot and drew rein. His eyes searched the opposite shore. He saw one place where he thought the animals could climb the slope. He waved his arm for quiet.

"Come, noble soldiers," he cried. "This is the first opportunity for you to show your courage."

He urged his horse forward and plunged into the stream.

Silence settled over the colony. Not even a child cried. All eyes were fixed on the figure in gray armor on the chestnut horse. Brown water rippled and curled around his legs. The horse whinnied anxiously as he felt the strength of the current. The listeners could hear Don Juan's voice encouraging the animal. In a few moments, the horse was scrambling up the bank on the other side. Don Juan waved and plunged into the water to return.

A great cheer went up. The camp broke into feverish activity. Directed by the Zaldívar brothers, men rushed on foot and on horseback to round up the animals. Shouts filled the air. Dust fogged the bank. Don Juan's horse clambered up the bank as the first cattle reached it. Seizing an ox-goad, the governor himself began driving the animals into the water. Pushed into the stream, the cattle raised their heads and started swimming toward the other shore.

Cristóbal watched breathlessly as the first wagon went down the steep bank. The horses reared in terror, but the teamster drove them into the current. With a lurch, the wagon plunged after them and sank low in the rushing water. In a moment, however, it bobbed up like a cork. The driver was now standing on the wagon tongue. The crack of his whip resounded over the water like a musket shot. Soon the horses were dragging the wagon up the bank on the other side.

In that way, all the wagons and carts crossed the stream. Only the sheep and a few straggling animals were left. The men started driving the sheep into the water. All was going well until suddenly, near the center of the stream, the lead sheep started sinking. The weight of their wet fleeces was dragging them down.

Discouraged looks passed among the men. The

sheep were needed for food and for starting flocks in the new land. Don Juan stood silent, studying the situation. Suddenly he announced that they must build a bridge. His men stared at him in bewilderment. How could they build a bridge?

"Bring two dozen of the largest wheels from the carts," the general ordered one group. To another, he said, "Chop down a number of the trees on the bank and trim them well."

When these things were done, two of the big cart wheels were lashed side by side onto rafts made of tree trunks. Two more wheels were tied to other logs and fastened to the first two. Two by two the wheels were added until the river could be spanned. Next, Don Juan ordered that the cart-wheel bridge be covered with branches, bark, and earth. In a short time, the men were watching proudly as the sheep came marching across the bridge.

The camp that night was full of praise for the courage and decision of Don Juan. Cristóbal must have felt very proud of his father.

Don Juan de Oñate was the first man chosen to establish a colony in New Mexico, but others had explored it before him. In 1540, Francisco Coronado entered New Mexico from the west through what is now the state of Arizona. After him, four other expeditions came by another route. They followed the

Conchos River until it flowed into the Río del Norte, which we now call the Río Grande. Then they turned northwestward, following it upstream to New Mexico. This was a long route, but it provided plenty of water.

Don Juan knew that it would be much shorter to travel straight north from the Conchos to the Río Grande, but this route presented two problems. The land must be level enough for the carts and there must be water for the people and the thousands of animals. He sent his nephew Vicente with seventeen men to search for such a trail. The daring Vicente endured many hardships and spent almost a month in the search, but he returned with good news. He had found a fairly level route which he thought had enough springs, water holes, and streams to provide water for the caravan.

Day after day, the expedition crawled northward like a long, lazy serpent. The advance guard had found occasional bands of Indians, but the people of the caravan saw none at all. Part of the way led across a grassy plain where the carts seemed like ships on a wide ocean. In March, they entered a long valley with a range of mountains on either side. They named the western mountains the Oñate Range. Watering places were plentiful in the valley, but after they left it water became more scarce.

On April 1, they started across the driest part of the trail Vicente had found. The day grew warmer and warmer. Soon the little water they carried was gone. Scouting parties set out in all directions looking for more. One by one they returned with bad news. No water anywhere. The day grew even hotter, and the heat increased the travelers' thirst. The train crept on. Men and women plodded silently ahead. Talking irritated their parched throats. The only sounds were the creak of saddle leather, the occasional wail of a child begging for a drink, and the shriek of the cart wheels.

Late in the afternoon, a bank of clouds appeared on the northern horizon. Everyone in the train watched as the clouds rose higher. The northern sky grew dark and forbidding. The dust-stained faces of the travelers filled with hope. Horses and oxen walked more briskly. A cool breeze struck the marching line. Then came a strong, cold wind that swept the dust in clouds about them. Sand stung their faces and burned their dry lips. The cloud mass now reached above their heads. The low sun, shining from the southwest, painted the underside of the cloud a weird rose color. It was like an upside-down sunset.

Suddenly, it began to rain as if buckets of water were being emptied from the sky. Women and chil-

dren huddled in the shelter of the carts and wagons.
Men pulled their cloaks over their heads and humped
their backs, like the animals, against the sting of the
cold rain. Shivering under his wet coat, Cristóbal
watched puddles form and join together to make
bigger puddles. Falling drops splashed on the surface like dancing figures.

The rain lasted until almost sunset. Then it moved
on across the plain, snuffing out the sun like a candle
as it went. Cold and wet as they were, the colonists
were very happy. The great pools of water would be
enough for all the animals as well as the people.
Being cold and wet was better than suffering from
thirst.

Father Martínez, the leader of the priests, appeared when the colonists were setting up camp. He
asked the people to join him in giving thanks to God.
Water dripped from the sleeves of his brown habit
as he raised his arms.

Colonists, soldiers, officers fell to their knees on
the wet ground. They felt that the rain was a miracle,
showing God's blessing on the expedition. After
that, they always spoke of that April 1 as the "Day
of the Miraculous Shower."

CLAIMING
NEW MEXICO
FOR THE KING

The morning sun looked down on a busy camp on the Río Grande a month later. Leather chests and boxes were scattered around the tents of the wealthy members of the expedition. Women were delving into these chests, taking out silk gowns and laces. Men rummaged for velvet doublets and wide hats trimmed with feathers. Servants ran back and forth, shaking the wrinkled finery and hanging it on the lower branches of the cottonwood trees. Mesquite and rabbit brush, too, bloomed with bright colored clothing. In other parts of the camp, the rest of the colonists were also getting ready. Soldiers polished their armor, while the women smoothed the wrinkles from their travel dresses. Don Juan de Oñate had decreed that the colonists should wear their best clothing on the next day, April 30. It was a day when history would be made. On that day, he planned to take possession of the new land for His Majesty, King Philip II of Spain.

The expedition had reached the Río Grande nine days before. After resting for a while, the travelers moved up the stream. They found a place where the river valley became wide and flat with distant hills on both sides. Sandy banks sloped gently down to the water. There Don Juan ordered the camp set up in a grove of cottonwoods and willows, whose new, yellow-green leaves twinkled in the spring sunlight.

Immediately carpenters and servants were set to work building a rough shed in the grove. This would serve as a chapel where church services could be held. There the expedition would be blessed before the ceremony of taking possession of the land.

The colonists chatted as they unfolded their finest garments, and their talk turned to the clothes they would wear the next day. Some of them wondered what Captain Luís de Velasco would wear. Everyone knew that he had brought several elegant suits, with forty pairs of boots and shoes! His servants boasted that his best suit, of blue Italian velvet with wide gold trimming, would be the finest one at the celebration.

Next morning the sound of a trumpet, instead of a church bell, rang through the grove to call the people to mass. At that moment, the little grove saw something it had never seen before and would probably never see again. Gowns of silk and satin swept the sandy earth. Fine laces fluttered as the ladies passed on their way to the chapel. Lace ruffs above velvet doublets and trunk hose graced the elegant figures of many of the men. Captain Velasco's blue velvet doublet and breeches, worn over green silk stockings with points of gold lace, was indeed the most elegant outfit to be seen. But the most dignified and impressive person was the gray-haired General de Oñate, dressed in black velvet with a white lace ruff. Cristóbal wore the same costume of black and white.

Inside the rough chapel, the company knelt on cushions or cloaks. Servants and herdsmen knelt on the bare ground outside. After the mass was over, Father Martínez preached a long sermon. He reminded his listeners that the first reason for settling a colony in New Mexico was to make it possible for the priests to win the Indians to the Christian religion. He told them that priests had already died for their faith in the territory. Three missionaries, who had remained after Coronado returned to Mexico in 1542, had been killed by the Indians in far-off Quivira. In 1581 three more priests had left New Spain to carry the word of God to the Indians of

New Mexico. Word had come back that these three had also been killed. By the time Father Martínez had finished, the faces above the silk and velvet garments were serious and fearful. What were they facing in this new land?

The dark fears aroused by the sermon were forgotten, however, in the feasting that followed. Fish from the river and wild ducks and geese shot by the hunters were roasted over big fires, along with half a dozen sheep and two beef cattle. It was a great day. The colonists enjoyed it to the full. Talking with their friends, they lived over again exciting times like the Day of the Miraculous Shower. The boys of the camp, Cristóbal among them, explored the grove and the river banks. Gazing across the rippling water, they tried to imagine what they would find in New Mexico. To them and to the grownups alike, it seemed as if their hardships were over and only good times lay ahead.

In the afternoon, officers and soldiers withdrew to put on their armor. Don Juan had ordered that the army was to assemble in full battle dress for the ceremony of claiming the land.

The little army looked quite imposing when it was drawn up on the plain outside the grove. Each company was lined up behind its captain, with its banners fluttering in the breeze. The sun glinted on polished armor, peaked helmets, spears, and halberds. The horses, many of them with steel plates protecting their faces and chests, pranced under the tough bullhide and buckskin armor that hung about them.

Vicente de Zaldívar, riding a sleek black horse, headed the army that day. His brother Juan waited with the priests near the grove. The field commander and the priests were to act as witnesses to the ceremony. They must sign a report to be sent to King Philip, telling him how the general had taken possession of the land in the name of His Majesty.

Don Juan de Oñate walked to the edge of the grove and faced his people. Silence fell over the chattering colonists. Even the children were impressed by the dignity and fine bearing of their leader in his armor of polished steel hammered with gold and silver.

In resounding Spanish, which sounded like men marching, Don Juan began to speak. He told his listeners how he had been chosen to lead the expedition. He reminded them that they had opened up a new and shorter road which could be followed by others. He spoke at length of the Indians in the new land and what he planned to do for them.

"And now, in the name of the most Christian king, Don Félipe, our lord, defender and protector of the holy church," he said, "and in the name of the crown of Castile, I take possession of the River of the North with all its meadows and pasture grounds and passes. This possession is to include all other lands, pueblos, cities, villages, of whatever kind now founded in the province of New Mexico, and all neighboring and adjoining lands. I take command from the edge of the mountains to the stones and sand in the rivers and the leaves of the trees," he concluded, holding his hands high as if to bless the new territory he was claiming.

The trumpeters blew a great, golden blare of sound, and the soldiers fired a salvo from their harquebuses. As the smoke drifted out across the valley, Father Martínez came out of the grove carrying a cross. Reverently he presented it to Don Juan, crossed himself, and joined the group of witnesses. With his own hands, the general nailed the cross to a tree and knelt before it. Earnestly he prayed that God would lead the Indians to accept the Christian religion and give the Spaniards peaceful possession of the land.

When the prayer was finished, a gray-bearded man stepped forward, carrying a magnificent flag. Golden cords bound it to its staff. Richly embroidered on one side was the coat of arms of His Majesty Philip II.

On the other was the emblem of Spain with its golden lions and castle towers. The man who carried this banner was Captain Francisco de Sosa, the royal standard bearer to whom King Philip had given the honor and the responsibility of carrying His Majesty's flag in the expedition.

Captain de Sosa handed the flag to the general. Don Juan lifted it before the cross as another blast of trumpets and crash of guns sounded. He then stuck the sharp point of the flagstaff into the ground nearby. As he bent his knee before it to show his loyalty to his king, a little breeze lifted the folds of the flag. Its shadow drifted over the general as if it brought good wishes from His Majesty. Father Martínez came forward and blessed the banner. Don Juan returned it to Captain Sosa, who held it high before the people. For a moment, the little plain was quiet as the colonists and soldiers looked reverently at the things that meant most in their lives—the cross of the holy church and the flag of their country.

The rest of the afternoon was filled with fun and excitement. The feeling of being on the edge of something wonderful was in the air. The women gathered in groups, chatting. Soldiers and officers laid aside their armor, now hot under the April sun. Many of them thronged about General de Oñate, talking eagerly about what lay ahead. Near the carts, some of the young soldiers had tossed a blanket on the ground and were playing dice. Vicente de Zaldívar and Captain Aguilar, a tall, brown-haired captain born in Spain, put their armor back on and started a contest. With the butt ends of their lances, they were trying to see who could first knock the other off his horse.

But not everyone was out in the grove and the plain. Some of the men and a few women had stolen mysteriously away. They could be seen moving around the carts and wagons which were drawn up at a distance from the grove. People began to look questioningly in that direction.

They did not have to wonder long about what was happening. Suddenly a trumpeter came marching from the wagons. The notes of his instrument rang clear above the noise and chatter. Everyone stopped talking. The soldiers left their game and crowded close. The trumpeter stopped and shouted an announcement. People looked at one another in surprise, their eyes brightening with interest. The man had invited them to a play!

They hurried forward. A makeshift stage had been made by moving aside some of the carts. Men, women, and children crowded about it. Cristóbal and the band of young explorers arrived, eager to see the performance. Don Juan was there, looking pleased and proud. It was good that his people should show an interest in the arts.

The play began with an introduction by a brown-bearded officer, Captain Farfán. He said that he wanted to honor the expedition and its leader by giving them a glimpse of what might happen in the new land. For this reason, he had written the play they were going to see. Many of the captain's fellow officers looked at one another in surprise. They had not known that Captain Farfán, who had proved his courage on many missions, was also a poet and a writer of plays. They looked at him with new respect.

The play began with two priests leaning on staffs and carrying crosses as they trudged across the small stage. Back and forth they walked, stumbling now and then to show that they were very tired. The audience knew the soldiers who were acting the part of the priests. They laughed when one of them stepped on the hem of his robe and almost fell. Then another young soldier appeared, dressed as an Indian, his face painted with streaks of white. He hid behind a high-wheeled cart, watching the approach of the priests. When he saw the cross, he left his hiding place and ran to the missionaries. He dropped to his knees and kissed the cross, explaining that other men dressed like these priests had taught him its meaning. He begged the priests to come with him to teach the true religion to his people. So the play went on, showing that the priests were gladly received, that many of the Indians were baptized, and that they were taught a new life along with the new religion.

The sun had set before the play was over. A bank of dark clouds looked gloomy and forbidding against the golden light in the west. A cold wind breathed down the valley. The colonists drifted away to their fires and their tents. They had thoroughly enjoyed this day of celebration. But now, feeling the cold wind, watching the darkness settle in this unfamiliar place, many of them must have felt their happiness slipping away. What would the new land hold? Were there really golden cities in this desolate country?

MYSTERY AMONG
THE PUEBLOS

Indians!

The word flashed through the camp. Everyone stared up the valley at a group of soldiers returning from a scouting trip. Four strangers walked in the lead with Vicente de Zaldívar. As they came closer, the colonists could see that they were muscular, copper-skinned men with black hair. Three of them were naked. The fourth, taller and more powerful than the others, seemed to be a chief. He wore a light blanket tucked around his waist like a short skirt.

The chief came toward Don Juan with his hands outstretched, palms upward, in the sign of friendship. Don Juan returned his greeting and led the way into a nearby tent. Whispering excitedly, the colonists waited to see what would happen.

How the visitors had changed when they emerged! Three of them strode out wearing Spanish shirts and breeches. The chief was more elaborately dressed.

He wore a doublet with trunk hose. Occasionally he patted them and laughed. It was clear that he thought the clothing ridiculous. But not the Spanish hatchet that hung at his belt. The Indians lifted their gifts from time to time and ran their thumbs along the blades.

When they left, General de Oñate invited them to send their friends to the camp. He could not be sure they knew what he was saying, because the Mexicans he had brought as interpreters could not speak the language of these Indians. Later in the day, however, eight more Indians came to the camp and were loaded with presents. In return, they led a party of Spaniards to a ford used by the Indians of the region. The discovery of the crossing was great news. The air in the camp fairly crackled with excitement. At last, the travelers were about to enter the land they had heard so much about!

The ford they saw the next morning is the place where two cities now stand on the Río Grande—El Paso in Texas and Juárez in Mexico. To the west, the river flows through a pass between steep, dark hills. Then its valley widens. At the site of the old ford, the water flows wide and shallow between gently sloping banks.

The lead wagons were about to enter the water that May morning of 1598 when shouts and whoops sounded ahead. A band of Indians appeared from behind a nearby hill. Their bodies were streaked with red, black, and white paint. The headdresses on their short, cropped hair were blood red. Long bows and quivers of arrows were slung over their shoulders. Cristóbal and the rest of the colonists must have felt their skin prickle, their hearts pound. Did these fearful looking visitors come in peace or war?

Quickly, the general ordered the chest of gifts brought up. He opened the lid and lifted a handful of beads that sparkled in the sunshine.

Excited chatter broke out among the Indians. They spoke words that sounded to the Spaniards like "amigos," the word for friends. All hands were out-stretched. The colonists sighed with relief as their visitors crowded around to receive the beads, whistles, and little mirrors that were handed out to them.

Soon the crossing of the river was under way. The Indians watched with interest as carts and wagons splashed across the ford. When the turn came for the animals, they joined in driving the cattle and sheep into the water.

Before leaving, Don Juan asked them, by signs, about the settlements that lay ahead. One man squat-ted on the ground and traced a map in the sand. Then he made the sign for a day's journey, which he repeated seven times. The officers nodded. Their tanned faces broke into smiles. A journey of eight days might lead them to a golden city!

Again the squalling cart wheels shrieked to the wind that the colonists were on the march, and the wind carried the news far and wide. A long mountain loomed above them on the right, and rough hills rose to the left. After a while the country flattened to a wide valley. The caravan was following an Indian trail close to the river. Its many cuts and dry stream beds made rough going for carts and wagons.

No settlements had appeared by the end of eight days of travel. Don Juan realized that the expedition, with its carts and animals, was traveling much more slowly than the Indians would have done. However, he needed to know when they would reach the first Indian town, or pueblo. Accordingly, he summoned Captain Aguilar, with a detail of six men, and assigned them a special mission. They were to scout ahead and locate the first settlement. As soon as it was sighted, they were to return with their report. They were forbidden to enter the pueblo. Don Juan explained that he must be able to bargain with the Indians for food, which was needed for the wagon train. He was afraid that they would become frightened and hide their corn if they were disturbed before his arrival. Sternly the general warned the men again that they must not enter the pueblo. Captain Aguilar bowed obediently. The next morning, the detail rode away toward the north. The wagon train followed, bumping slowly along over the rough trail.

In a few days, the scouting party returned. They had found the first settlement! The delight that swept the camp soon changed to disappointment. News leaked out of the council in the general's tent that the pueblo was not a golden city. The men described it as a pile of mud. The feeling of disappointment was followed by one of amazement and horror. The rumor spread that Captain Aguilar had been sentenced to death! He had disobeyed his orders and had entered the pueblo. People said that Don Juan, white with rage, had snatched his sword from its sheath when he learned the truth. Only the interference of his officers had prevented him from executing the captain then and there.

Captain Aguilar was popular with the expedition. So the officers and priests began to plead with Don Juan to spare his life. They pointed out that Aguilar was a brave and fearless man. They reminded the general that he would need all his men for the work ahead. At last, Don Juan promised to consider their pleas.

The next day the general's Negro servant, who acted as a crier to make public announcements to the people, appeared in the center of the camp. After a shrill blast from his trumpet, he shouted that, due to the mercy of the governor, Captain Aguilar would be pardoned. The colonists were greatly relieved. For a while they forgot their disappointment.

This experience taught Don Juan that it would be best for him to lead an advance guard to explore the land. Such a party could travel rapidly, and he would always be in control. He selected sixty of his best men and two priests, Father Martínez and Father Salazar. Juan and Vicente de Zaldívar were among the group, of course. Another was round-faced Captain Villagrá, whose beard and heavy mustache were gray though he was only thirty years old. He had been appointed to write a history of the expedition. Cristóbal must have been excited when his father told him that he, too, could ride with the party.

The general named Captain Francisco de Sosa as his lieutenant-governor in charge of the rest of the army and the wagon train. Then the advance guard struck out into the rough, waterless country ahead. Mesquite bushes and cactus spines tore the skin of horses and the boots of riders. Their water was used up on the second day. Men and horses plodded on, their throats dry and parched. Suddenly one of the dogs appeared with muddy feet. With a shout of joy, the men scattered, searching for the water the animal had found. The two waterholes they discovered enabled both men and animals to quench their thirst. Soon after, the trail led back to the river, where traveling was easier.

On the morning of the seventh day, they began to see fields of corn, squash, and cotton in the valley of the river. Irrigation ditches carried water to the crops. Surely they must be near the pueblo!

Early in the afternoon they were able to see it on the high ground across the river. From the distance they could tell only that is was two stories high, and they knew from Captain Aguilar's men that is was constructed of mud bricks. A number of Indians watched them from the flat roof of the second story. There were no signs of welcome.

The Spaniards passed without stopping. Ahead of them, on the east side of the river, a second pueblo was visible. As they drew near, they saw that it was larger than the one they had passed. In some places the massive houses were three stories in height. Suddenly they noticed that numbers of Indians were running away from the town into the valley. Don Juan halted his army and called again for the chest of gifts. The Indians stopped, too, and they stood staring at these men whose clothing glittered in the sun.

The general dipped into the chest. With his hands dripping with beads and little bells that tinkled as he moved, he started toward the nearest Indian. The man hesitated, ready to run. Another man behind him, however, started toward the enticing presents. Others began to inch cautiously forward.

Cristóbal now had his first look at some of the Pueblo Indians among whom he would spend several years of his life. Many of the men wore tunics of cotton or deerskin, like long shirts without sleeves. Others wore woven cotton cloth like a skirt reaching to their knees. Their black hair hung in braids beside their copper cheeks. The women watching from the back wore cotton garments, too, tied over the left shoulder and held in place by a woven belt. Many of the dresses and skirts were embroidered in bright colors.

After giving presents to everyone courageous enough to come near, the general ordered camp to be set up in the river valley. He reminded his men that the king had instructed them to treat the Indians well at all times. His plan was to gain the confidence of the Indians by showing them that the strangers would not harm them. In this way, he hoped to be able to bargain with them for corn.

In a few days, the plan began to work. The pueblo

dwellers were curious. More and more of them came to stare at the visitors, peer into the cooking pots, and gaze fearfully at the horses. The chief came, too, and Don Juan was able to obtain several bushels of corn. He needed more, but the chief made signs that seemed to mean that his storage bins were empty. Fearing that he did not understand, Don Juan sent for his interpreters. Once more, they shook their heads. This language was different from that of the Indians at the ford, but they did not understand it either. Clearly, the Indians of this territory spoke several dialects. Don Juan wished with all his heart that he had someone who knew this speech.

As the Indians became more friendly, the Spaniards began to return their visits. Cristóbal's heart must have thumped with excitement the first time he and his father entered the pueblo, which was called Qualacú. Passing through an entrance at one corner, they found themselves in an open space. Each side of this square, or plaza, was filled by one large communal house two or three stories high. Cristóbal looked at them curiously. Each story of the buildings was set back from the roofline of the one beneath. In this way, a terrace was formed at the second story level all around the square. Cristóbal watched a number of Indians climb the ladders that led up to this terrace, where they stood staring down at their visitors. For a moment he wondered why everyone was going to the upper floors. Then he saw that there were no doors or windows in the first floor. So the only way to enter the pueblo was by climbing a ladder!

Looking around, he saw something else that puzzled him. At either side of the plaza the end of a ladder protruded from a hole in the hard-packed ground. While he was wondering about this, some of the older Indians came forward to greet the visitors and show them around the pueblo. The first place they were taken was to one of those ladders. Cristóbal could then see that it disappeared into an underground room. He learned that this was the kiva, a chamber where many religious ceremonies took place and where the men and boys spent much of their time. No women were allowed there. The guides led the way up the ladders to the second story. Don Juan and his son peered into small, whitewashed rooms where the people lived. They learned that the first-floor rooms, entered by trap doors, were used to store grain, beans, and dried squash for the winter. Cristóbal looked with interest at the stones piled at the edge of the roof. No one needed to tell him that they were there in case of an enemy attack.

After two weeks, the Spaniards started eagerly on their way. Seeing Qualacú had convinced them that somewhere this civilization must have developed into a rich society. More than ever they felt sure they were marching toward golden cities. The weather became hot as the days passed, and the mountains to the north and east seemed to grow taller. They had the good luck to find one pueblo where they were able to get a large quantity of corn to send back to the train. They named the place Socorro, the Spanish word for "help." A town with the same name stands now near the site of the old pueblo.

After Socorro, they began to find the pueblos deserted. News of the strangers with firesticks and shining clothing had spread up the valley. The Indians preferred to hide until the newcomers had passed by. On the afternoon of June 23, more river bottom fields told the marchers that they were approaching still another pueblo. This one, too, was deserted. The rooftops were empty, with the ladders still standing against the walls. Since the next day was a religious holiday, the general decided to camp near the pueblo. Religious services would be conducted, and the marchers could rest for a day. He also hoped that the Indians would return as they had at Qualacú.

As he had hoped, the Indians began to drift back the next morning. By the time Father Martínez had finished his sermon, the rooftops were swarming with them. Visitors from other pueblos had also come to see the strangers.

During the afternoon, the Spaniards celebrated the saint's day with a sham battle. Vicente led one group and Juan the other. The two small armies faced one another in a meadow in the valley. A crowd of Indians stood under the trees, plainly wondering what was going on.

With ear-splitting yells, the armies charged one another. Horseman rode for horseman, each trying to unseat the other. Spears clanged against steel armor. Shields clashed. Several men limped away as prisoners of war when they were thrown from their horses. Finally, with a grcat ycll, Vicente's force swept over Juan's army, seized the men who had been captured, and charged up the slope above the valley. There they fired their harquebuses as a sign of victory. The crash of guns reverberated up and down the valley.

Many Indians ran away at the noise. Others, however, stood their ground. Their dark eyes darted here and there, trying to drink in these strange events.

Don Juan was congratulating the winners when three Indians approached. One of them, a thick-bodied man, spoke to the general.

"Thursday, Friday, Saturday, and Sunday," he said in Spanish.

The Spaniards stared at him, as astonished as if one of their own horses had spoken. They crowded around, urging the man to say more. He repeated his words, but that was all he could say.

What a mystery! Someone had taught this man a few words of Spanish. Who could it be? Don Juan felt that he must learn more about this. He signalled the soldiers who were on guard. Soon the Indian was surrounded by soldiers carrying spears and harquebuses. He shrank back in fright.

"Tomás. Cristóbal," he said desperately, pointing to the north.

The Spaniards stared at one another. Those were Spanish names!

Again they crowded around, trying to ask by signs where Tomás and Cristóbal were. The Indian seemed to understand. He pointed again to the north. He made the sign for a day's journey and repeated it.

Two days' journey! Two days would lead them to men with the Spanish names of Tomás and Cristóbal. (This Cristóbal will be called Tobo after this to avoid confusion.) Perhaps these men had been with one of the earlier exploring expeditions. Perhaps they would know the Indian language of this part of the territory. In that case they could be the interpreters who were so badly needed. Don Juan was already making plans to solve the mystery.

The pictures
in the kiva

The eastern mountains looked like cardboard cutouts against the pink sky when the expedition set out next day. Father Martínez' morning prayer had been longer and more serious than usual. Everyone knew why. They were on their way to Puaray, the pueblo which the Indians said was two days' journey away. It was also the place where Father Rodríguez and Father López had been killed. These two priests and another, Father Santa María, came to New Mexico in 1581. After visiting several pueblos, they decided to live in Puaray and teach Christianity to the Indians there. So pleased were they with the way the Indians received them that Father Santa María started back to New Spain to invite other priests to join them in the work. On the way, he was killed by another Indian tribe. The two who remained died later on in the village they had thought so friendly. No one knew how they had been killed, but a servant who escaped brought the news of their death back to Mexico.

From the faces of the men around him Cristóbal guessed that they, too, were thinking about the missionaries. They looked at Father Martínez and Father Salazar as if they wondered how the priests would feel when they entered the pueblo. Perhaps the men who killed the good fathers still lived there. It was a sobering thought.

They reached Puaray late in the afternoon. The pueblo sat on the high plain above the river. Its broad mass, three stories in height, glowed a brownish yellow in the light of the setting sun. In the distance, it looked like a golden city. The tired bodies of the Spaniards straightened in their saddles. Eyes began to sparkle with excitement.

A closer view, however, showed that this pueblo was built of the same brown mud and stones as the others they had seen. The excitement in the men's eyes gave way to a look of wary caution as a throng of people poured out of the town to meet them. They were led by a tall man whose hair hung in long, gray braids. He wore an embroidered cotton tunic. Ornaments of bone and tails of small animals dangled from its hem.

Don Juan and his chief officers dismounted. Accompanied by the priests, they went to meet the

Indians. At either end of the group, soldiers carried flags that snapped in the afternoon breeze.

The tall Indian held up his hand when the two groups met. He spoke to the visitors in a guttural voice which sounded like stones clashing together. In a level gesture, his hand showed the pueblo on its flat plain. He raised his arms, and his moving fingers indicated the peaks of the mountains beyond. He was welcoming the Spaniards to his town and the surrounding lands. When he had finished, several Indians came forward. Four of them carried a big clay jar filled with dry corn from last year's harvest. Others brought sheafs of green corn from the summer crop. Still others carried live turkeys with their feet tied together. These gifts they laid at Don Juan's feet.

The general, in turn, made a speech. He thanked the Indians for the gifts. He told them that he came in peace seeking two men named Tomás and Tobo. Nodding heads showed that the men were known in the pueblo. Don Juan ended by signalling for the chest of gifts, from which he chose presents for the chief and the other leaders of the pueblo.

By means of signs, the chief then invited his visitors to enter the village. Vicente and a number of men turned back to pitch camp for the night. The general and the priests walked toward the pueblo

with the chief. Juan de Zaldívar and Cristóbal followed with a group of officers. The chief led them
through a narrow passageway into the open plaza
between the buildings. This pueblo was much larger
than the one at Qualacú, but otherwise they were
much alike. A squaw brought out blankets and
spread them on the ground. Seating themselves, Don
Juan and the Indian leader began their talks. When
the general mentioned Tomás and Tobo once more,
the chief shook his head. They did not live in Puaray,
though the Indians of this pueblo knew who they
were. He pointed north and indicated by signs that
the two were in Santo Domingo, another pueblo
farther up the valley.

Their talk finished, the chief made a sign of going
to sleep and pointed to the interior of the pueblo.
Don Juan tried to answer, also by signs, that he must
rejoin his men. Father Martínez and Father Salazar,
however, nodded that they would accept the invitation. Cristóbal was shocked, though he tried not to
show it. He knew that the priests were always ready
to offer their lives in their missionary work, but how
could they go calmly into this pueblo, remembering
what had happened here? He watched with worried
eyes as the brown robes of the two men disappeared
following an Indian guide.

Early the next morning, the priests came hurrying with grim faces to the Spanish encampment. They hardly seemed to hear the greetings of the soldiers as they passed. They went straight to the general's tent. A feeling of uneasiness swept the camp at their unusual behavior.

A short time later, Don Juan called the men together to let them know what had happened. The two priests told the story. The night before, they had been taken to a small, neatly swept room with a floor of packed earth. The walls were still wet from a recent whitewashing. After their evening prayers, the fathers had gone to sleep, believing that God had softened the hearts of the Indians of Puaray.

The next morning the walls were dry. Faint lines were visible through the whitewash. These proved to be Indian drawings that had been painted over but now showed through. Curiously the priests examined the walls. They found several hunting figures and some animals they recognized as deer.

Suddenly they stared at one section of the wall and then looked at one another. There could be no doubt about what they saw. The kneeling figures holding crosses were priests. The figures standing over them with upraised war clubs were Indians. One of them had his hand drawn back in the act of throwing a stone. It was a crude picture, but its meaning was clear. Father Rodríguez and Father López had been beaten and stoned to death.

There was muttering among the soldiers when they heard the story. Men reached for their harquebuses as they glared angrily toward the pueblo. They did not understand, of course, that the Indians were protecting their religion as the Christians would protect their own. They had no way of knowing that the Indians were afraid the teachings of the strangers might anger their gods and bring punishment down upon them. They had felt that they must get rid of the priests to avoid such a disaster.

General de Oñate calmed his men. He reminded them once more of the king's orders that the expedition should keep peace with the Indians. He promised that they would stay in Puaray only until they could find the men they were seeking. He and the field commander would lead a detail to Santo Domingo that very night. He ordered his soldiers in the meantime to keep watch over the fathers as they tried to teach the Christian religion to the Indians of Puaray.

"But do not let the Indians suspect that we have seen the pictures," he said earnestly. "You must never stare at them."

The soldiers followed these orders exactly as they awaited Don Juan's return. The next day, the gen-

eral and Juan de Zaldívar came triumphantly back to
Puaray. By a forced march, they had reached Santo
Domingo at dawn. An Indian of the pueblo pointed
out the house where Tomás and Tobo lived. The
Spaniards found the two men still sleeping and
brought them to the general. As he had suspected,
they proved to be two Mexican Indians who had
entered New Mexico with one of the earlier exploring parties. When the expedition returned to New
Spain, they stayed behind. They had lived with the
Pueblo Indians for several years and spoke the
language of this part of New Mexico.

What a lucky find this was! At last, the Spaniards
could really talk with the Indians of this region. They
could tell the Indians that the king of Spain wanted
them to become part of his empire. They could explain the laws and regulations of that empire. Now
the missionaries could have help in teaching Christianity. Indeed, from every point of view, the finding
of Tomás and Tobo was most fortunate for Don
Juan.

The general set to work at once to use these men
as interpreters. He wanted to have the surrounding
pueblos at peace before the arrival of the colonists.
After they came, he knew he would be busy settling
the people in their new homes and organizing his
government. Therefore he sent out a runner to several

nearby towns. The runner carried a leather notebook belonging to Don Juan to prove that he was the true representative of the general. The chiefs of the towns were invited to meet the Spaniards in Santo Domingo on the seventh of July. This pueblo was chosen as the meeting place because it was the one whose language Tomás and Tobo knew best.

The morning of July 7 found the central square of the pueblo thronged with people. The chiefs who had answered the summons had brought other men with them from their own pueblos. Most of these were the respected old men who made up the tribal councils. Their dark eyes were thoughtful in their wrinkled faces, for this was a solemn occasion. Chiefs and council members alike wore their finest robes of embroidered cotton or deerskin. One man had a long necklace of turkey bones. Others wore ear pendants and necklaces of shells and chunks of turquoise.

After attending mass in their camp, the Spaniards came marching into the plaza. Standard bearers with the flags of Spain and of King Philip led the way. Behind them came General de Oñate and his two nephews, all wearing their finest armor. The brown robes of Father Martínez looked very humble beside their splendor. Behind them strode the rest of the captains and soldiers.

Across the plaza they marched to the great kiva,

which was partly underground. Circular walls about six feet high stood above ground. One ladder protruded through a trap door in the roof and another, shorter one led from the roof to the ground. Without hesitation, the Spaniards mounted the ladder one by one, climbed to the roof, and disappeared into the interior of the great council chamber.

This was the first time that Cristóbal had been inside one of these secret chambers. He looked around curiously. It was difficult to see what the room looked like because of the dim light and the crowd that waited there. He could tell, however, that the roof was supported by great beams resting on four pillars. On one side he caught a glimpse of what looked like an altar against the wall. Then the beginning of the ceremony demanded his attention.

First, Don Juan called the interpreters before the royal secretary. He was a gray-bearded man whose forehead was marked by a scar that seemed to glow in the dimness. The big, leather-bound book before him contained the king's record of all the important happenings in the colony. Tomás and Tobo stood before him and took a solemn oath to translate truthfully what was said.

With Father Martínez standing beside him, Don Juan spoke to the Indians. He told them that the Spanish king wanted to bring them into his kingdom

to teach them the Christian religion and also to protect them from their enemies. He asked them to become subjects of King Philip of their own free will and to promise to obey his laws.

Tomás and Tobo translated his words into the Indian language. Then the seven chiefs who represented pueblos in that region talked together, discussing what Don Juan had said. Next, each of them called the members of his council into the discussion. Gray and black heads drew close together as they talked. Finally, the chiefs faced the governor and said that they had chosen to become subjects of the king. Don Juan reminded them that, if they became vassals of King Philip, they would be expected to obey his laws and would be punished if they failed to do so. They nodded solemnly. They understood, they said, and still wanted to become subjects of the great king. Tomás and Tobo repeated their words to the general.

As a last step, Don Juan explained that the most important reason for the coming of the Spaniards was to bring them the true religion. He said that Father Martínez was the leader of the priests who would teach them this religion.

The chiefs nodded again. They were ready to accept both the Spanish rule and the Christian religion. Don Juan asked them to show their sincerity by kneeling to kiss the hand of Father Martínez in the name of God and his own hand in the name of His Majesty, the king.

A deep silence fell over the crowd in the sacred kiva. The only sound was the whisper of the moccasins across the hard-packed floor as each chief approached and knelt before Father Martínez and Don Juan in turn. When they rose from kissing the general's hand, Juan de Zaldívar handed each of them a staff of office to show that he was now a lieutenant in the empire of King Philip. The chiefs accepted the gift proudly and returned to their councilmen, where it was passed from hand to hand and examined curiously.

Probably none of the Spaniards present realized that, in spite of their efforts to make the matter clear, the Indians might not understand exactly what they were doing or what they were promising. For those armor-clad men, the conquest of New Mexico had begun gloriously!

MUTINY IN THE CAPITAL

The New Mexico colony now had a capital! It was a pueblo on the banks of the Río Grande given to the Spaniards by the friendly Indians who lived there. They had gone to live in a nearby pueblo with others of the same tribe. The Spaniards renamed the pueblo San Juan. Farther Martínez blessed it and sprinkled holy water at the four entrances and over the altar in the kiva. The Spanish flag was run up over the headquarters of Governor de Oñate. So the place lost its Indian name of Ok-he. On July 11, 1598, it became San Juan, the first capital of the first permanent colony in what is now the United States of America.

Hardly were his men settled in the narrow, little rooms of the pueblo when Don Juan called them together for a council meeting. There they made enthusiastic plans to continue their explorations. Many pueblos and tribes were yet to be visited. The men hoped to be able to report to the rest of the colonists, when they arrived, that the dream of golden cities had come true. They were ready for great adventure when they assembled for the march. Their horses were groomed. Their armor was shining. Even their boots, torn by cactus and scuffed by sharp rocks, had been rubbed with grease until they looked like new.

The Indians of San Juan told Tomás and Tobo that other pueblos were to be found farther up the Río Grande. As they marched along its banks, the soldiers kept a sharp eye on the stream bed. They were watching for ore that might have been washed down by the current. Several times the glint of shiny pebbles in the water sent the men scrambling off their horses and down the bank. One soldier found a small stone about half the size of his fist. It was heavy, and its color was dull yellow.

Unfortunately, it was the only one of its kind found on the entire journey. In the following days, the Spaniards went north as far as Taos. There tall Indians watched them from the tops of two large buildings, six stories high, on either side of a sparkling mountain stream.

After a quick return visit to San Juan, the explorers traveled east as far as Pecos. This was the strongest and best fortified pueblo they had yet seen.

Its four-story houses stood behind a stone wall on a long, flat-topped hill above the Pecos River. But the houses were made of brown earth and rock, like the others. Its proud people looked indifferently at the samples of gold their visitors showed them. They knew nothing about such a metal.

Retracing their steps, the Spaniards crossed the Río Grande and toiled up the rough canyon of the Jémez River. Located in narrow cuts near its headwaters was a group of eleven pueblos. The visitors found a friendly people who brought them food and water as they struggled up steep hills. But the journey, so difficult that several horses slipped off the precipitous trails, failed to reveal any wealth.

After almost a month, the general led his men back to San Juan. Their boots were now worn thin. The once shining armor was scratched and dented, and the heads wearing the peaked helmets drooped a little. But the confident ones told each other that this was only the beginning. They had been in New Mexico less than four months. Wait until four years had passed, they said. Then they would know better what they had found. There were others, however, who were ready to give up. They had seen nothing in the new land that they wanted.

Then something happened to arouse new hope. One day the soldiers on guard brought in a small, dark man dressed in rags. They had found him wandering near the pueblo, and he had spoken to them in Spanish!

The man told the governor that he was a Mexican named Jusepe. He had come into New Mexico in 1593 with an exploring party led by Captain Bonilla and Captain Humaña. Don Juan knew about that party. In fact, the king had ordered him to arrest the leaders if he found them, because they had entered the territory without the king's permission. But the party seemed to have vanished. Nobody knew what had happened to it. Now, at last, Don Juan learned its fate. Jusepe told him that the group had marched far to the east to a region called Quivira. Then one day, in a fit of anger, Captain Humaña killed his fellow captain. This act frightened Jusepe. He ran away, only to be captured by a tribe of wandering Plains Indians. While living with them, he heard that Captain Humaña and all his men had been destroyed by the Indians of Quivira. Later, he learned of the coming of other Spaniards to New Mexico. He escaped from his captors and finally managed to reach the new colony.

The arrival of Jusepe delighted the general. He would now be able to report to the king the fate of the rebel captains. Better yet, he had found an interpreter for future explorations, for Jusepe had learned the language of the Plains Indians. Don Juan questioned him closely about Quivira. The man told of rich and fertile land, with large settlements of Indians. When asked about gold, Jusepe said that he had seen none in the places he visited, but that he had heard of lands farther on where the metal was abundant. So once again, the dream of golden cities was revived.

One day in mid-August, the south wind brought a strange sound into the camp. It was a far-off wailing, like cats fighting in the distance. The men at San Juan listened with question marks on their faces. Then, suddenly, they recognized it. It was the squalling of the cart wheels. The wagon train was arriving at last!

In a short while, the pueblo was filled with the noise of children, the lowing of cattle, and the blatting of sheep. Gaunt men and women shook the dust from their clothing and gazed at the new capital. Some of them saw the beauty of the green valley and the sparkling stream. Others looked bitterly at the brown earth of the pueblo and muttered under their breath.

Governor de Oñate welcomed them with a feast which began, of course, with a speech. He described the explorations of the advance guard and praised the generosity of the Indians in giving up the pueblo. Pointing with pride up the valley, he showed them a line of small figures working under the broiling sun. These were soldiers, with a large group of Indian helpers, who were digging an irrigation ditch. It would bring water to the fields where the colonists would plant wheat and other crops. He spoke of the tasks that lay ahead of them. The first thing, of course, would be to build a church. Father Martínez had already chosen the location and work would begin at once. When that was done, they would start building houses for the families. These plans seemed to encourage the faint-hearted. Soon the walls of the pueblo were echoing to the sound of laughter and Spanish music.

The following days were busy ones. Men went to the mountains to cut logs for the church. Father Martínez tucked up his robe and rushed here and there, supervising the Indians as they made adobes. Soon long lines of these earthen bricks lay drying in the sun. In a week, the building of the walls began. In the meantime, the women, aided by servants and children, unpacked the carts and settled their families in the pueblo.

As the days passed, however, it became clear that some people were not interested in the work being done. Small knots of men could be seen in earnest conversation under the cottonwood trees or down on the river bank. Tall, handsome Captain Aguilar was often one of them. People began to notice that the talk stopped suddenly when any one else came near. A feeling of uneasiness began to grow, as if a dark cloud was forming above the camp.

One day late in August, the storm broke from that cloud. Disturbing rumors filled the settlement. People gathered in fearful groups, discussing in low voices what they had heard. Captain Aguilar and two other men were under arrest as leaders in a plot to desert the colony and return to Mexico! Some one whispered that the governor knew the names of all the forty-five men involved in the scheme.

Forty-five men! The faces of the loyal colonists turned pale. That was more than a third of the fighting men of the expedition. Such a loss could be fatal to the colony if the Indians turned hostile. Besides, the colony had a contract with the king himself. Would it not be treason to desert? And what about Captain Aguilar? His life had been pardoned once before. How did he dare to lead a mutiny?

Gloomy days followed, though the work went on. The church walls rose higher and higher. Day by day the irrigation ditch crawled a little closer to the capital. But tension and uneasiness gripped the settlement. All day, missionaries and army officers could be seen going in and out of Don Juan's quarters. Again they were pleading with the governor to spare the men under arrest.

One afternoon, the sound of the trumpet and the ringing voice of the crier called all the colonists to meet in the plaza. Everyone hurried to the meeting, where they waited silently in the hot sun. Even the children were quiet, their eyes round as they watched.

Juan de Zaldívar and Father Martínez appeared on the first floor roof. Juan spoke to the people. He told them that the governor had studied very carefully the case of the three men. They had convinced him that they were plotting an expedition of their own to search other pueblos for gold. This was not permitted under the law, but the governor had pardoned their mistake. They would be set free at once.

People cheered wildly. Women laughed and cried with relief. Men pressed forward to thank Don Juan or to speak to the former prisoners. When the happy clamor began to die down, Father Martínez raised his arms for silence. He announced that the work on the church had gone so well that the building could be dedicated on September 8. The mass and the dedication ceremony would not be the entire celebration, however, he added with a smile. There would also be feasting and entertainment to which the Indian leaders of the region would be invited. The colonists were delighted. It was great to have a fiesta to which they could look forward. All friction and discontent seemed to melt away at the prospect.

The sun had just climbed the eastern mountains on the eighth of September when the clanging of a bell called the Spaniards to the church service. This bell, brought by the priests from Mexico, hung from a tree because the bell tower was not yet ready. The governor had again asked his people to dress in their best. So, to the amazement of the Indians, velvet doublets and dainty silk dresses paraded across the bare plaza. This time, however, some of the velvet was spotted and the laces yellowed by summer rains that had seeped into the chests. And many shoes that showed beneath the silken skirts were worn and scratched.

The church was ready for its great day. The women had searched their trunks for embroidered cloths to cover the rough altar. Buckets of wild flowers, picked by the children, stood on either side. The roof was not finished, but the bare rafters had been covered with leafy branches to keep out the sun.

The service lasted all morning. Father Martínez blessed the new church, the altar, and the chalices. Then Father Salazar preached a long sermon. He reminded the people that the purpose of the colony

was the advancement of the kingdom of God, not their own profit. Captain Aguilar and the others accused of plotting against the colony seemed not to see the many glances that came their way.

For the children, the afternoon was much more exciting. There were tilting matches, where mounted riders tried to knock one another from their horses. A play was presented in the grove of cottonwoods. But the event most eagerly awaited was the battle between the Moors and the Christians. This contest represented the long struggle of the Spaniards to drive the Moors out of Spain. All these battles ended the same way, but they were always exciting.

The two armies faced one another on the level plain behind the pueblo. The Moors were on horseback, carrying spears and shields. The Christians were on foot, swords and daggers at their sides, harquebuses in hand.

Juan de Zaldívar, leader of the Spanish army, snatched his sword from its sheath. Waving it above his head, he shouted the battle cry of the Spanish Christians. The Spanish army ran toward the enemy. The Moors galloped to meet them. The two sides met in a cloud of dust. The Spaniards tried to drag the Moors from their horses, and the enemy tried to fell the Spaniards with their lances. Dust swirled about the struggling figures. Shouts rang across the field, punctuated by an occasional shot fired into the air. At last, the battle ended with the Moors fleeing across the plain, chased by the Christians. A volley from their harquebuses announced their victory. The noise and smoke from the guns also announced to the Indians the power of the newcomers.

The ceremonies of the next day centered about the Indian visitors. Several pueblos that had not been present at Santo Domingo were represented in San Juan. For that reason, another ceremony of accepting the Spanish rule was held in the kiva. Once again, Don Juan de Oñate explained the presence of the Spaniards. Once more the chiefs kissed the hands of the governor and Father Martínez to show that they accepted the Spanish king and the Christian religion.

This time the ceremony did not end there. Don Juan went on to tell the chiefs that they could learn the new religion more easily if they had priests living in their villages. The chiefs replied through the interpreters that they would welcome the coming of the fathers. Father Martínez then brought out a list he had prepared and started assigning the priests to the different tribes. Cristóbal listened soberly. All these men would be going into distant pueblos he had not seen. They would see no familiar faces. They could not even use their own language. For the first time, the boy fully realized what it meant to wear the brown robe and the sandals of the Franciscan fathers.

As Cristóbal emerged into the open air through the trap door of the kiva, the odor of roasting beef and fresh-baked bread swept all sober thoughts from his mind. Now it was time for the feast, to which the Indians, too, were invited. Everyone was moving toward the great cooking fires on the plain behind the pueblo. Only two Indians were going in the wrong direction, down the river bank away from San Juan. Both Spaniards and Indians shouted to them, with no results. They continued on their way without turning their heads. Some one said that they came from Acoma, a strong pueblo far to the west. Few people guessed that they had come as spies to study the activities of these strange newcomers to the Indian lands of New Mexico.

The humpbackeD cattle

Only a week had passed since the dedication of the church, but again San Juan was buzzing with activity. Soldiers with armloads of armor and blankets hurried to a line of pack mules waiting outside the plaza. There other men packed the saddle bags and lashed burdens on the backs of the animals. Officers shouted to servants to bring swords or extra bridles or horse armor. Women directed the packing of food into large leather bags. Children, darting in and out, were scolded for getting in the way of the grownups. The reason for all the excitement was that an exploring party of about sixty men was preparing to leave San Juan. Vicente de Zaldívar, with Jusepe as interpreter, was leading them to explore the buffalo plains to the east.

Cristóbal must have watched enviously as the expedition made its preparations. He had heard many tales about the "humpbacked cattle," about how fierce they were, about how the ground shook when a herd stampeded. What boy of thirteen would not have wanted to see them for himself? Besides, his favorite cousin was leading the party.

At last, the expedition was ready. Vicente's black horse pranced at the head of the line. The two priests mounted on mules beside him were Father San Miguel and Brother Juan de Dios. They would travel with the army as far as the pueblo of Pecos. There they would take up the duties which Father Martínez had assigned them in the kiva the week before.

Cristóbal thought again of the fortress-pueblo and hoped that it did not seem so frightening to the priests as it did to him. It was good that Brother Juan knew the language of the Pecos people. That should make life easier for them. The boy watched the brown robes and the man on the prancing horse until they were blocked out by the long line of pack mules, herdsmen, and mule drivers.

To many of the men, the trail was familiar as far as Pecos, for they had followed it with General de Oñate only two months before. An uneventful march of four days brought them to the pueblo. Immediately Father Miguel and Brother Juan climbed the hill and disappeared behind the pueblo wall. The rest of the Spaniards camped in the river valley below. They

spent the next day visiting the pueblo, talking with
the chief, and exploring the valley of the Pecos River.
On the second morning, the priests returned to the
camp. Father San Miguel said mass for the men,
blessed them, and prayed for their safe return. After
saying goodbye to the fathers, they turned their
horses toward the east.

The third day after leaving Pecos, they came upon
a small stream. Fish could be seen like darting sha-
dows in its clear waters. The men rushed for the fish
hooks, which were always a part of their equipment.
The fish were biting that afternoon, and soon they
had caught a large number. Then the cooks went to
work. Officers and soldiers lounged on the cool grass
waiting for the feast.

Suddenly one soldier sprang for his gun. The
others followed his example. Striding toward them
along the river bank came four tall men. They were
evidently Plains Indians, for they wore only breech
cloths and moccasins. Hanging from a strap that
crossed one shoulder was a long bow and a quiver of
arrows. They extended their right hands, palms open
to the sky.

Vicente watched them closely and decided that
they seemed friendly. He called for the pack of gifts
he had brought. The Indians happily accepted the
small mirrors, beads, and ribbons that were given to

them. While his companions squinted into the mirrors, one Indian stood up and gave a loud cry.

The Spaniards were startled. Again they gripped their guns and prepared for trouble. But the group of fifteen or twenty braves who appeared as if by magic from the bushes along the bank also came forward with outstretched hands. Soon they, too, were gazing with pleasure into the mirrors and admiring the ribbons.

With the help of Jusepe, Vicente asked about the country ahead. Then he inquired whether any man of their tribe would be willing to guide the Spaniards to the land of the humpbacked cattle. To his delight, one of the group offered to lead them himself.

The party made good progress with the new guide. He strode without hesitation across the trackless land, promising that they would soon reach the buffalo. And he was right. In a short time they saw their first buffalo bull. The guide explained that the animal was alone because he was too old to keep up with the herd. The buffalo looked so awkward with his high hump and the billy-goat beard under his chin that the Spaniards burst into laughter. But their horses did not find the animal funny. The buffalo lowered his huge head and pawed the earth, glaring at the horses through the thick hair hanging over his eyes. They reared and snorted and tried to run away.

In the next few days, the travelers saw a number of small, scattered herds. The buffalo interested Vicente and his men so much that they began to talk about taking a few back to the colony. Vicente thought it would be possible to build a corral into which they could drive some of the animals. The men liked the idea. As they rode, they made plans for the corral and discussed the advantages of having a herd near the capital for the wool, hides, and meat, which they had heard was very good.

The guide kept telling the party that they would soon come to a region where the entire prairie would be covered with buffalo. So eager was Vicente to find the large herds that he went ahead with the guide and ten men to locate them. On the way back to camp, they visited a village of the Plains Indians. These people followed the buffalo, moving as the herds moved. The tall, athletic braves stared curiously at their visitors and even more curiously at the horses, but they showed no fear. They allowed their guests to roam through the camp at will. Vicente and his men observed with interest that the buffalo supplied almost everything these people used. The teepees were made of buffalo hides. Other hides were used as beds. The moccasins they wore, the bands that held their black hair out of their eyes, the skirts of the women were all of buffalo hide. Even the needles and thread came from the animals. The needles were of sharpened bone. Thread was made of thin strips cut from the hides or of tendons from the bodies of the beasts. The visitors were especially impressed by the softness of the tanned leather. The guide told them that it was just as soft after it had been wet. Finding this hard to believe, Vicente cut a piece from a tent flap and soaked it with water from his water-bag. He called his men to see it after it was dry. They were amazed to find it as pliable as it had been before.

Shortly after the arrival of the Spaniards, the Indians began to take down their tents. The buffalo had moved from the place where they were now living, so the Indians had to go, too. The visitors were surprised at the speed with which the teepees were taken down and the hides folded for moving. They stared with amazement when they saw how they were transported. The women caught the shaggy dogs that roamed about the camp. Tent poles were lashed along their sides and on the poles were loaded the hides, dried buffalo meat, and camp equipment. The Spaniards watched, open-mouthed, as the animal dragged their loads after their masters across the plain.

Rejoining his men, Vicente led them across the river which we now call the Canadian. On the level prairies beyond, they saw at last the great buffalo herds the guide had been promising them. In spite of all he had said, they could hardly believe their eyes. The wide, green plain was covered with what looked like a dark brown carpet, which flowed and spread as the herd moved in its grazing. The astonished Spaniards estimated that there must be at least one hundred thousand of the animals. This was certainly the place to build their corral.

Everybody plunged into the task. Officers who seldom worked with their hands followed the example of Vicente. Some chopped down small trees near the river. Others trimmed off the branches. Servants and drovers dug holes for placing posts in the prairie soil. With such a large labor force, the corral was finished in three days. It was built with two long wings flaring from the gate toward the open prairie. Once the buffalo entered these wings, the narrowing walls would act as a funnel to force them to enter the gate.

The corral finished, they were now ready for the cattle. A small herd was grazing just east of the corral. Vicente divided his men into three groups. One detail was to circle the herd until it reached the opposite side. They were the drivers, who would start the buffalo toward the corral. The other two groups were to ride to the north and the south to keep the animals headed along in the right direction.

Everything started according to plan. The drivers rode toward the herd at full gallop, shouting as they came. The guard bulls on the fringe of the herd raised their heads at the noise. Then they turned and raced away from the danger. Like a well-oiled machine, the herd turned with them. Straight toward the waiting corral they ran. The men relaxed, sure that all was going well.

Suddenly some warning seemed to reach the buffalo. Instinct must have told them that trouble lay ahead. They swerved to the north toward Vicente and the men riding that side.

At once, the Spaniards charged into action. Leaning forward over the necks of their horses, they raced toward the animals, shouting at the top of their lungs. Every moment they expected the oncoming herd to swerve again toward the corral. But the buffalo did not turn. On they came across the prairie like a huge brown rug gone mad.

The shaggy beasts were almost upon them before the Spaniards realized that they could not turn the herd. Whirling their horses, they fled for their lives. Vicente, who had been in the lead, was closest to the animals. He had almost reached safety when a fast bull caught up with him. Vicente saw the upward jerk of the great head. The horse lurched, and

Vicente knew that it was gored. The horse recovered its stride, however. With a great leap, it cleared the path of the stampede. Then it stopped, its legs trembling. Vicente found that the horns of the buffalo had ripped the horse's flank and side. Fortunately, the wound was not deep. It would heal, but his favorite horse could not be ridden for many a day. A few yards away, the last of the herd pounded past on its mad flight. It was clear that they were not going to enter the corral that day.

Vicente and his men did not give up easily. For several days they kept trying to drive the buffalo into the corral. Finally, after three horses had been killed and a large number wounded, they decided that it was impossible to corral the animals. Someone suggested that they catch some of the calves. It would be easy, they thought, to take back young ones who were not so wild as the adult animals.

By this time, the buffalo had moved several miles away. Skilled ropers rode out to the herds. Before the mothers knew what had happened, a number of calves were seized by the circling lariats and dragged away. Some of the men pulled them along at the end of the ropes. Others tied them across the horses behind the saddle.

Vicente, who was as skilled as any of his men, was one of the ropers. He caught a fine buffalo calf and tied it on his horse. At first, it struggled to break the ropes that bound it. After a while, however, it became quiet. On the long ride back to camp, Vicente realized suddenly that the calf had not moved for some time. He turned in his saddle. The buffalo calf was dead!

Vicente dismounted and examined it. It had not been choked. It had no wounds. It had simply died. Vicente looked around. Other men had stopped, too, and were staring in surprise at the limp bodies behind their saddles. The same thing had happened to the calves that were led by the ropes. Not one had lived more than an hour after it was captured. The only explanation was that they had died of fright.

After this last disappointment, the men gave up. They continued on across the treeless plains hunting the buffalo. When the pack mules were loaded with meat, tallow, and hides, it was time to return to San Juan.

They retraced their steps across the plain and crossed the river near which they had built their corral. The days were still sunny and warm. But the nights were becoming so cold that the men shivered under their blankets and buffalo hides. After several days of marching, they began to see the mountains in the west and felt they were nearly home. On November 8, they reached San Juan.

The colonists crowded around to hear about their adventures and to admire the buffalo-hide teepee that Vicente had brought back. The Zaldívar brothers were happy to be together again, though it would be Juan's turn to leave the capital in a few days. He explained to Vicente that Governor de Oñate was away with another exploring party visiting a region in the south which the Spaniards had not yet seen. A few days before, a messenger had come from the governor with orders for Juan.

"Stay in San Juan until Vicente returns from the buffalo country," Don Juan had written. "Then leave him in charge of the settlement and follow me with thirty well-armed men equipped for a march to the South Sea."

The "South Sea" was the name then used for what we now call the Pacific Ocean. No one knew how far away it was, but they did know that it would be a long, cold march. The field commander set his thirty men to mending their thickest boots and preparing their warmest clothing and blankets. During the preparation, the brothers had time to talk about everything that had happened to them both.

Finally, the detachment was ready. They set out from San Juan on November 18. Little did Vicente think, as he waved goodbye that cold, windy morning, that he would never see his brother again.

CORN MEAL AND MINES IN THE WEST

With Cristóbal at his side, General de Oñate marched west from Puaray in late October. The Spanish force looked very small in the immense brown land it was entering. But the spirits of the men were as gay as the pennants that fluttered above them. Somewhere ahead lay the South Sea. And, according to tales that circulated in Mexico, pearls had been found in that sea. Behind the army, too, the situation was pleasant in Puaray. The men had seen the robes of the priest there gripped by the trusting fingers of Indian children. Their elders also listened with what seemed like respect when the father talked with them. The dark shadow of the pictures on the kiva wall seemed to be lifting.

Day after day, the Spaniards marched westward. Dry stream beds slowed their progress. Sentinel mountains watched them from the west and north. Four days of travel brought them to a region of steep-sided, rocky mesas. One of these was an irregular mass of white rock towering 357 feet into the air. On top of it stood the pueblo of Acoma, as it still stands today.

The Spaniards gazed wide-eyed at three-storied houses on top of the mesa. This must be a powerful tribe, they told one another. How could a sky city like that ever be conquered? In his report to the king, Don Juan described the place. He said that it contained over five hundred houses and that the only path to the top consisted of hand holds and footholds worn in the solid rock.

When the Spaniards reached the mesa, they found that their approach had been watched. The chief, dressed in a turkey feather robe, was at the base of the cliff to meet them. Down the rocky ladder, the people followed as fast as they could. They pointed excitedly at the horses. Fifteen years had passed since any Spanish expedition had visited Acoma. The children, therefore, had never seen the animals.

While Don Juan, aided by Tomás, held a conference with the chief, the men put the horses through their paces. The Indians watched with amazement as they reared and pranced. Some soldiers rode toward groups of Indians and laughed to see them scatter in fear. The general put an end to that sport by announcing that the chief had invited them to visit the pueblo.

The climb was hard for the Spaniards. Boots slipped from toeholds where moccasined feet had no trouble. The heavy harquebuses slung on their backs weighed them down, but they could not risk going unarmed. Even Cristóbal, who was not burdened with a gun, found himself panting when at last he stood beside a pile of rocks on the top of the mesa. He looked with respect at those rocks, thinking how easy it would be to knock a climber off that rocky ladder.

At a signal from Don Juan, the harquebuses were pointed skyward and a salute was fired. The salvo was intended to impress the Indians, but the wide plain surrounding the mesa seemed to swallow up the sound.

The chief, with several young braves, escorted the visitors along the narrow streets between the houses. At the end of the village, they pointed out their water supply. Rain, caught in natural pools in the rock surface, provided all the water they needed. Next they led the Spaniards up to the roof of the first story of one row of houses. Here the top of a ladder projected from a trap door. One of the men spoke to Don Juan, pointing to the ladder. Tomás explained that the Indians were inviting him to visit their kiva, where they kept their greatest treasure.

Don Juan stepped forward to accept the invitation. Suddenly he stopped. Perhaps he distrusted the darkness into which the ladder descended. Perhaps there was some movement below. At any rate, he hesitated a moment. Then he turned to Tomás and asked him to tell the Indians that the general must lead his troop back down to the plain. There would be plenty of time to return afterward to see the treasure.

Don Juan did not know then that he had saved himself from death. He learned later that twelve Indian braves were hidden in the kiva, ready to strike him down.

The plot to kill the Spanish leader had failed. But the Acomans gave no hint that they had planned to attack their visitors. Women brought water for the camp in jars carried on their heads down the steep path. Men came with gifts of corn, turkeys, and melons. When Don Juan asked them to declare their loyalty to the king of Spain, the chief knelt and kissed the general's hand. Cristóbal must have watched the ceremony with a special interest. His father had appointed him to serve as a witness on this occasion. He probably felt quite grownup when the secretary wrote the name "Don Cristóbal de Oñate" first in the list of witnesses.

The Spaniards left the pueblo without realizing the danger they had escaped. Two days beyond Acoma, the weather began to change. Lead-colored clouds appeared, dragged along by cold winds. Sharp flakes, half snow, half ice, began to fall. Soon the little army was walled in by a curtain of snow.

Fortunately, they were near a well-known camping place. This was a sandstone cliff which the Spaniards called El Morro. Today we call it Inscription Rock. Indians, Spaniards, and later travelers made camp at Inscription Rock because it offered three things they needed—shelter, water in a natural basin at its foot, and firewood from scrub pines and bushes on the surrounding plain.

Soon a big fire was roaring at the base of the cliff. The horses had been fed and watered and left with a guard nearby. The men stretched their stiffened fingers toward the fire and sniffed with pleasure as the cooks began to prepare supper. Suddenly, they heard a disturbance among the horses. Dimly, through the snow, they could see the nearest horses rear in fright, though they could not see what had caused it. Then the pounding of hooves told them that the animals had stampeded. They disappeared like dark ghosts into the swirling snow that made it impossible to pursue them. It was a discouraged group of men that sat around the fire that night.

Next morning, however, things looked brighter. The snow had stopped, and a detail went out in search of the lost horses. The men returned before noon, bringing most of the runaways. The animals had huddled in the shelter of a small hill not far away. There were enough mounts to continue the march. Accordingly, Don Juan detailed three soldiers to find the rest of the animals while the remainder of the army moved on.

Shivering in the cold as they marched next day, the Spaniards were happy to see another Indian pueblo in the distance. This must be Zuñi, they said to one another. Coronado had to fight to enter it when he came into New Mexico almost sixty years before. But other expeditions had come and gone peacefully since then. How would the people of Zuñi receive these new visitors?

They did not have to wait long to find out. Soon they spied a long line of Indians approaching from the pueblo. Soldiers gripped their harquebuses. Officers loosened the spears in their stands. They continued to march forward, tense and alert.

Making gestures of peace, the Zuñis drew near. Suddenly the Spaniards stiffened in their saddles. Their fingers tightened on their weapons. The Indians were reaching into some skin bags they carried. Perhaps they had hidden weapons. . . .

Before anyone knew what was happening, men and horses were showered with something like flour. Cristóbal had the stuff in his hair, in his eyes, in his teeth. But he and the other Spaniards rubbed their eyes and grinned. They had been in New Mexico long enough to know that corn meal was sacred to the natives. The unexpected powdering was the Zuñi way of showing friendship and blessing their coming.

The Zuñis proved their friendship in another, more useful way. As the Spaniards passed, a woman emerged from each house to present them with a blanket. These gifts were greatly appreciated, for the visitors were not prepared for the cold of this high plateau country. The Indians also invited their guests to take part in a community rabbit hunt. In spite of Don Juan's caution that this might be a trick, his men joined in the great circle of hunters and enjoyed themselves thoroughly.

There were many other things to do besides enjoy the hospitality of the Zuñis. Captain Farfán was sent to explore some salt springs near the pueblo. He had hardly gone when an Indian came running to the general, pointing toward the east. Tomás explained that the man had sighted a group of four white men approaching with some horses. Don Juan was puzzled. He had left only three men behind. He and Cristóbal rode out to meet the group. They

recognized the horses and the three men. But who was the fourth? His cheeks were hollow above the gray beard. Sunken eyes looked out beneath the peaked helmet. With a sudden start, Cristóbal realized that this was no stranger. It was Captain Villagrá!

The captain's story sobered his friends. Returning from a special mission on which Don Juan had sent him, he learned that the general was on his way to Zuñi. The captain followed, expecting to overtake the force and make his report. He planned to stop in Acoma for food, but he found the Acomans so hostile that he hurried on. Camping that night on the trail, he was awakened by snow in his face. Since he could not sleep, he decided to ride on. The trail was so clear that he felt sure he could follow it, even in the snow. He had gone only a short distance when his horse lurched forward, whinnying with fright. Horse and rider crashed through a covering of dry branches and fell into a deep pit which had been dug in the trail.

Stunned for a moment, the captain could not understand what had happened. Then he realized that the pit must be the work of the Acomans. He must not be caught there if they should examine their trap the next day. He tugged at the horse's reins, but there was no answering movement. The poor animal had been killed in the fall.

There was no time to mourn his loss. He must get out of the pit, but he could not climb weighed down by his armor. Sadly he left it on the body of the horse. Clawing with his fingernails and kicking toeholds with his boots, he managed to climb out of the pit. Then, weak from fright and lack of food, without armor, he set out on foot to follow the trail.

The soldiers found him, nearly dead from hunger and cold. His friends embraced him when they heard his story and thanked God for his escape. But it was hard for them to believe that the Acomans had dug the pit. Why, they had taken an oath of loyalty to King Philip only a few days before!

Thoughts of Indian troubles were soon blotted out by more pleasant things. Captain Farfán, returning from the salt springs, enthusiastically said that he thought they must be the best in the whole world. The Zuñis told their visitors of another Indian tribe farther west and of minerals in the mountains not far from their pueblo.

Once again the Spaniards marched west. They found the next tribe, which we call the Hopis nowadays, quite similar to the Zuñis in their houses and their way of dressing. Like the Zuñis, these Indians, too, received the Spaniards as friends and were glad to give them information about the mines. To find these mines, the general appointed Captain Farfán, Captain Quesada, and a detail of seven men. Then Don Juan led the rest of his small force back to Zuñi to wait for Juan de Zaldívar. He was beginning to be worried because Juan had not yet arrived. The order to follow had been sent to him some time before the governor left Puaray.

Early in December, Captain Farfán and Captain Quesada came galloping back to Zuñi, bubbling with good news. In several Indian villages, they had seen powdered ores which the natives used to paint their bodies. The Indians guided them to the mines from which the ores had come. They traveled for days through mountains, sometimes with snow up to their knees. Finally, they reached their goal. The Indians had only scratched the surface, but the ore they had uncovered looked rich and promising to the Spaniards. They staked a number of claims at the site. They also saw shells, which looked like pearl-bearing oyster shells, hanging from the foreheads and noses of some of the Indians. These people said that the shells, when opened, had something like a white bead inside and that they came from a sea far to the southwest.

It was no wonder that General de Oñate could not sleep that night. He lay awake for hours, staring into the darkness. At last, the future looked bright. If the mines proved even half as rich as his captains thought, the success of the colony was assured. And the news of the pearls was also very encouraging. Thinking over the situation, Don Juan decided to postpone the journey to the South Sea. It would be too risky to attempt it without the reinforcements from San Juan. He would return to the capital and make sure that all was well. There he would have time to make plans for both the development of the mines and the journey.

A few days later, the Spanish force was again marching toward Acoma, this time from the west. Captain Farfán rode on one side of the general, and Captain Quesada's red beard flamed on the other. Everyone, from the general down to the lowliest herdsman, was pleased with the success of their journey. Besides, Christmas was less than two weeks away and they were on their way back to their friends and families. The men sang and joked as they rode in the winter sunlight.

One afternoon they caught sight of a dust cloud on the trail ahead. They thought it must be Juan de Zaldívar and his men coming at last. As the groups approached one another, Cristóbal could see that the other was, indeed, a group of Spanish riders. But it was too small for the thirty men his cousin Juan was supposed to bring.

Riding at a gallop, the two groups were soon within hailing distance. Don Juan's men shouted a greeting. There was no answer from the seven riders coming toward them. One of them spurred ahead of the others. It was Captain de las Casas. His black hair and beard framed a somber face as he stopped in front of Don Juan.

"My General," he said, his lips white, "I have to tell you that the field commander and ten of our soldiers were killed in Acoma on December the fourth. The Indians are in revolt."

WAR WITH ACOMA

General de Oñate and his men stared in shocked silence at Captain de las Casas. For a moment, the only sound was the creak of saddle leather. Don Juan spoke first. His voice was hoarse with grief when he asked what had happened.

The captain told the story briefly. The field commander had reached Acoma early in December. He and a group of his men went to the pueblo to ask for corn meal and other provisions for their journey. They promised the Acomans hatchets, bells, and iron goods in exchange for the food. The Indians told them to come back the next day, when the meal would be ready. The commander did as they asked, returning with eighteen men and some servants. The Acomans accepted the trade goods, but they sent the Spaniards to different parts of the pueblo to collect the meal. When the Spanish force was divided, the Indians fell upon the men with war clubs, stones, and arrows. The Spaniards fought bravely, but they were greatly outnumbered. Three men escaped down the cliff. Five jumped from the top of the rock. Four of these survived, as though by a miracle. The rest were either killed or forced off the cliff to their death. Captain de las Casas ended by saying that there was no doubt that the Indians were still on the warpath. They had killed several of his horses from ambush as he came to break the news to the general.

A gloomy group of men ate cold rations and rolled into their blankets without a fire that night. The general had retired sadly to his tent, asking not to be disturbed. The tramp of guards around the camp beat out the hours. Cristóbal, his eyes red with weeping for his cousin, must have thought about the wide land beyond the sentry's round. The country was so vast, their little camp so small.

By morning, the general had overcome his sorrow for the nephew who had been so close to him. Although his voice broke once in a while, he spoke to his men, giving orders for the return march through hostile territory. Scouts were sent far ahead to watch for any suspicious movement. The most heavily armed men were appointed to lead the way and bring up the rear. Sentries were to be doubled in the camp at night. Probably because of these measures, the party had no trouble with Indians and marched steadily ahead toward the capital.

As soon as Don Juan was sure they had passed the danger zone, he sent Cristóbal ahead, accompanied by Captain Villagrá and Captain Quesada. They were to ride as fast as possible to notify Vicente that the general and his force were returning safely. The entire settlement was in mourning when the three riders reached it. The grief of the colonists was deepened by the fear that other tribes might follow the example of the Acomas. The people looked fearfully at the Indian workers in the capital and the friendly natives of the neighboring pueblo. The first break in this atmosphere of sadness and suspicion was the news that the general and his army were safe.

The first problem Don Juan had to face was the question of what should be done about Acoma. Most Spaniards felt that the colony would be destroyed if this attack went unpunished. It was a case of Acoma or the colony. But the soldiers could not simply march against the pueblo. The Indians were the special wards of the Spanish king. No attack could be made against them unless it could be proved that such an action was necessary.

Accordingly, a court was set up to study the evidence. The men who escaped from the cliff and

others who had been on guard below described what
they had seen. The priests were asked whether a
war against Acoma would be just. The answer was
that a war fought to bring about justice, punish
criminals, or keep the peace was a righteous war.
These requirements seemed to be satisfied.

So Don Juan called his men to a council meeting
at his headquarters. There it was decided to march
against Acoma at once. The pueblo should be given
the chance to surrender the men who had killed the
Spaniards. If they refused, the village would be attacked. The general wanted to lead the expedition
himself, but the people begged him not to risk his
life. The priests reminded him that he was respon-
sible for the fate of the colony. Finally, he yielded
and appointed Vicente as field commander in his
brother's place. It would be his duty to lead the
Spanish force against Acoma.

Vicente set about with grim determination to prepare his army of seventy men for their campaign.
Since they would march in the dead of winter, they
must take their warmest clothing. Leather doublets
and heavy hose were inspected. Boots were mended
and rubbed thickly with grease. The heavy harquebuses were cleaned. Powder was measured into large
containers to be carried on pack animals. The powder flasks of the men were filled, great care being

taken not to waste a single grain. Two small cannons were strapped onto carts to be taken along.

It was January 12, 1599, when the army set out from San Juan. Th entire settlement turned out to see it go. Everyone ╵ ╵ered when Vicente rode out to take his brother's place at the head of the troops. Then the watchers fell suddenly silent. Many days must pass before they would know the fate of those who marched away that day.

As it turned out, the colonists had little time for worrying. The very next morning, the governor's crier with his trumpet called the men to a hurried council meeting. Word had come from the neighboring pueblo that the Indians of that region were gathering to attack the settlement!

Though his heart sank at the thought of less than fifty men against a large Indian army, the general set up his defenses. He posted a guard detail at each of the four corner entrances to the plaza. A fifth group was a special guard which could move swiftly to any place where it was needed.

During the afternoon, Don Juan started across the plaza to inspect the guard posts. Suddenly he stopped and looked up. The roof tops were covered with people, mostly women. His brows drew together in a frown. Those people should know the danger from Indian arrows by this time! He called a captain and sent him to find out what was happening. In a few minutes, the man was back with the information that the wife of the king's standard bearer had organized the women to help protect the village. Aided by the children and servants, they had spent the day collecting stones and piling them on the roof tops, as they had seen the Indians do. The women intended to hurl the stones at any invaders that might come. The general's face relaxed in a smile of pleasure and pride. These were real Spanish women! He sent the captain with his warmest thanks to tell the women that they were appointed guards of the roof tops. As he went on with his inspection, his heart was lighter than it had been for days.

The night passed quietly in the little capital. The following day and night were equally peaceful. The lookouts could report nothing more suspicious than an occasional coyote slinking about the pueblo or a deer seeking grass that was not covered with snow. After the third day, the colonists decided that the threat had been a false alarm. Life in San Juan settled down to waiting for news.

More than two weeks had passed when three riders came spurring up the valley one day. They pulled their lathered horses to a stop in front of the governor's headquarters. Smiles of triumph cracked the caked dust on their faces as they reported that the battle was over. The Sky City had been conquered and almost destroyed.

Cristóbal must have listened with eyes, ears, and mouth open to the battle tales told by the soldiers. Like the rest of the colonists, he heard the stories so often that he came to feel as if he had been there.

He knew how the Acomans had received the Spaniards. They thought it so funny that only seventy men should try to attack their fortress that they howled with laughter. The Spaniards could see that their bodies were painted red, white, and black. Some wore the armor they had taken from the Spaniards they had killed. They shouted and screamed insults, secure in the belief that they were safe on top of their cliff. All night long, the noise of drums and whoops resounded over the plain as the Acomans danced their war dances.

The next day, as General de Oñate had ordered, Vicente called the interpreter to his side. Tomás shouted up to the Acomans the terms the Spaniards offered. If they would come down from the rock and surrender the men who had killed the Spaniards, only the guilty would be punished. If they did not, the entire pueblo would be attacked. The Indians answered with screams of rage and defiance. A shower of arrows, war clubs, and spears drove the Spaniards back from the base of the cliff.

From their camp at a safe distance, the soldiers gazed soberly at the Sky City. Could they possibly conquer such a place? The new field commander started out to study the mesa, hoping to find a solution to the problem. As he rode around it, he saw a place where he thought the cliff could be scaled by good climbers. It was a rocky point that could not be seen from the main entrance. A sudden idea struck him. He hurried back to camp and called his war council. His plan was that the army should attack the entrance to the pueblo. This would draw all the warriors to that spot. Meanwhile, a picked group led by Vicente himself would try to climb the cliff and gain a foothold on the top.

The plan was put into effect the next day. The Spanish force marched with banners flying toward the pathway to the pueblo. The Indians rushed to drive them back. Meanwhile, twelve chosen men, who were hidden near the point, started their climb. As they thrust the toes of their boots into cracks in the rock, they listened for the sounds of battle. They were safe as long as they could hear the war whoops and the crash of guns. When at last they could peer over the top of the mesa, not an Indian could be seen. The plan had worked!

They found that the rock on which they stood was separated from the rest of the mesa by a wide chasm.

The two sections were connected by a narrow, rough path that ran over huge boulders in the crack. Examining their position, the Spaniards discovered a break in this path near their side of the chasm. Looking ahead, they could see another. It seemed impossible for them, weighed down by their armor and heavy guns, to leap across these cuts. How could they reach the main part of the cliff?

While they pondered this problem, a shout reached their ears. They had been discovered! Arrows whistled around them. One man was knocked to the ground by a heavy stone, but he jumped up and joined his companions. A number of Indians ran single file along the pathway. Nimbly, they leaped the breaks that had stopped the invaders.

Quickly the Spaniards unlimbered their harquebuses. Before their fire, the Indians fell back. The detail was able to hold the rocky point it had gained.

Before night fell, Vicente climbed down the cliff. He planned to bring up more men in the morning and with them a beam to be used to bridge the breaks in the pathway across the chasm.

The reinforcements came scrambling up the cliff in the first light of dawn. Puffing, pulling, and tugging, they hauled up the trunk of a pine for a bridge. The pueblo was quiet. No movement was to be seen among the houses. What an opportunity! Excitedly, some of the soldiers seized the beam and rushed onto the pathway. They swung the trunk across the first break in the path. Thirteen of them rushed across and lifted the log to carry it on to the next.

Suddenly a band of Indians appeared from behind the boulders along the path. Harquebuses blazed. Some Indians fell, but the rest kept coming. There was no time to reload. Tomahawks and spears, swords and lances flashed in the morning light. Step by step, the Spaniards retreated to a line of protecting rocks.

The men on the point watched helplessly. They could see the log lying beside the path. But without it, they could do nothing to help their comrades. Vicente shouted for someone to go down the cliff and have another beam sent up. Two men scrambled to do his bidding.

Suddenly Captain Villagrá ran back to the edge of the cliff. There he turned and raced for the crevasse, gathering speed as he ran. Vicente grabbed for him as he flashed past. He missed. The captain reached the lip of the cut and gave a mighty leap. The few seconds that his body hurtled through the air seemed like an hour to the breathless watchers. If he did not clear the break, he would be dashed to pieces on the rocks below.

A great shout went up. He had made it! Hardly

had his feet touched the pathway when he seized one end of the pine log and pushed it across the crevasse. Eager hands took it and steadied it. In a moment, the soldiers were pouring across to the aid of their companions. The Indians fell back before their on-rush, and the day was saved for the Spaniards.

That was the beginning of the end for the brave and reckless Acomans. The Spaniards now had a secure foothold in the Sky City. Vicente de Zaldívar had his two small cannons hauled to the top of the cliff. The Indians had no chance against them, but they fought with unbelievable courage until their city was burned and a great many of their people killed. Over five hundred of them finally surrendered. They were marched to Santo Domingo, where they were put on trial as a lesson to the other tribes.

Their punishment was a cruel one. All children under twelve were held under the care of the Span-iards. Vicente de Zaldívar was put in charge of the boys and Father Martínez of the girls. All people over twelve were condemned to be slaves for twenty years, except the very old, who were released to other Indian tribes. In addition, all men over twenty-five were sentenced to have one foot cut off. There were not many of these, for most of the warriors had been killed on the Rock.

TROUBLED
TIMES

Two months had passed since the battle against
Acoma. Spring was thawing the frozen mud in the
plaza where the people were gathered. They had
come to say goodbye to another expedition leaving
the capital.

The men of this expedition were some of the most
important of the settlement. Captain Villagrá was
the leader. Enthusiastic cheers greeted him when he
appeared. Ever since the battle of Acoma, he had
been a hero to the people. His dark eyes sparkled
above his gray beard as he waved in response to their
welcome. Captain de las Casas, Captain Farfán, and
several other leaders were mounted and ready to go.
Father Martínez was going, too. The colonists
crowded about him to kiss his hand before he left.
With the usual blare of trumpets and fluttering banners, the group rode away to the south. The eyes of
many colonists must have followed them with envy.

They were on their way to New Spain. They were going "back home."

The reason for their journey was the rebellion of Acoma. That event had made the governor realize as never before the dangerous situation of his colony. He had spent long hours studying the matter and talking it over with his council. He knew now that he must keep a strong force to guard the settlement. This meant that he did not dare march to the sea in search of pearls. Neither could he spare soldiers to work the mines discovered by Captain Farfán. He must have more men. Father Martínez was to ask for more priests. His captains carried letters asking for more soldiers and supplies and explaining why they were needed.

Don Juan watched the group leaving. The fate of the colony rested on them and on the way they presented the case before the viceroy. Only when a bend in the river valley hid them from view did he turn again to his headquarters. When he saw a group of men waiting for him, he felt sure they wanted to remind him how scarce food was becoming in the capital.

He knew better than they the difficulties of providing food for the colony. Once a month, he sent soldiers from pueblo to pueblo to collect from the Indians the tribute which he demanded in the name

of the king. This tax was paid in blankets, corn, and
beans. At first the Indians did not object openly.
However, as the winter wore on and their supplies
grew scarce, they became hostile and indignant. The
angrier and more unwilling the Indians became, the
more ruthless the soldiers were in taking what was
demanded. The governor knew that he was respon-
sible to the king for the way the Indians were treated.
He also knew that it would be a long time before the
colony could support itself. He thought about the
three hundred twenty bushels of wheat he had
brought for seed. The colonists had used almost all
of it, leaving only about twelve bushels to be planted
when spring came. As a result, the harvest would
fall far short of the need. Don Juan went forward
grimly to talk with the delegation.

The months went slowly by. April and May
brought spring days and warm sunlight. The servants and some of the colonists planted gardens.
Indians planted the remaining wheat and corn along
the river for the colony. Food problems were not so
pressing now, but tension was growing in the settlement. The people had been drawn together during
the battle of Acoma and the days that followed, but
now they were becoming restless and quarrelsome.
No word arrived from the expedition. June came

and July. Still no word. The men grew more and more restless. The governor tried to keep them busy by sending small details to search the mountains for minerals. They went without enthusiasm and returned without having found anything worthwhile. The talk kept turning to the South Sea. The tales of pearls in those waters drew them like a magnet.

At last, Don Juan decided to send Vicente to explore a route to the sea. With him went twenty-five or thirty of the most impatient spirits of the camp. Once more hope flared in the colony. Everyone admired Vicente for his daring and his resourcefulness. Perhaps, in addition to the pearls, he might find a golden city on the shores of the South Sea.

So the colony settled back to wait for news from this party, as well as the one in Mexico. Gradually, the months crawled by. The leaves turned yellow on the cottonwoods in the valley. On the mountains, the distant groves of aspens looked like splashes of gold. The colonists reaped a good harvest from the few bushels of wheat they had planted. If only they had had more to sow!

The golden leaves were gone and the mountain peaks gleamed with the first snow when an excited herdsman raced into the pueblo. Mounted men were approaching from the west. It must be Vicente's party! The entire village came running to the plaza, pulling threadbare shawls and jackets about their shoulders.

Bitter disappointment awaited them. The men who reined their gaunt horses to a stop in front of the pueblo were as thin and hungry as their animals. They had wandered for three months, finding nothing but poor Indians living in brush huts. Worst of all, they never reached the South Sea. Rough mountains, lack of food, and hostile Indians forced them to turn back. Fate seemed determined to block the Spaniards from finding the wealth they sought.

There was nothing to do but keep on waiting for word from Mexico. Christmas that year of 1599 was a grim season, and the year that followed was even worse. Food, as always, was scarce. Many people were in rags. It was now two years since they had entered New Mexico. No wonder that a worn silk dress was often seen trailing its once proud skirt in the mud of the plaza, or an embroidered doublet worn as an everyday shirt.

Hunger, poverty, and disappointment made the colonists more and more restless and unhappy. Many of them must have felt they had been tricked into coming to New Mexico. The stories of wealth in the north had caused them to sell their property and leave their homes. And look what they had found, they said bitterly. Mountains, deserts, half-naked Indians! Their disappointment turned into resentment toward Don Juan as the leader of the expedition. Many of them talked openly about returning to Mexico. This talk frightened and angered Don Juan. It meant the destruction of the colony before there was time to complete the explorations. As a result, the trumpet of the town crier called the people one day to hear a decree issued by the governor. In this proclamation, Don Juan stated that no one could leave the colony or the army. The penalty for disobeying would be death!

Resentment against the governor grew even stronger after that. Open discussion about returning to Mexico was stopped. Instead, talk began to circulate about secret plots that were being hatched to escape. The camp divided into two factions— those who were loyal to Don Juan and those who wanted to break away. Tension and bitterness grew stronger with every passing day.

One morning, word passed like an electric shock through the settlement. Captain Aguilar was dead! The handsome, reckless captain had been popular with many people. The little capital was deeply grieved. But it was also troubled and perplexed. The report from headquarters said that the captain had been executed for disobeying the governor's orders. People remembered that Captain Aguilar had been sentenced to death twice before. But then the people had been informed, and the priests and army officers had been able to persuade Don Juan to be merciful. This time, there had been no word until the captain was dead. Ugly stories began to circulate that this was not a military execution but a murder plot contrived by Don Juan and his loyal officers. People talked in whispers when they met, glancing fearfully over their shoulders.

The pall of gloom grew worse a few weeks later when Captain Alonso de Sosa disappeared. Gossip said that the captain, who had brought to New Mexico fifty-eight horses and colts, eighty milk cows, sixty-five oxen, and seven carts to carry his other belongings, had asked permission to go back to New Spain. He said that all his fortune had been spent, and he must return to a place where he could support his family. One day he went out with other officers and some of the soldiers to round up the horses. When the party returned, Captain de Sosa was not with them. His body was never found.

Once again, the colonists did not know what had happened. Men on the roundup had seen the captain ride into a ravine. It was possible that he had been killed by an Indian hidden there. But some people said that he had been attacked by a group of soldiers and dragged away. No one else asked permission to leave. But that fact did not put an end to the desire to go. It only deepened the divisions within the settlement. The village seethed with hatred and hostility.

Those long, dragging months must have been very hard for Cristóbal. Hostile stares followed him everywhere. People he had thought were good friends turned their backs on him when they met. He saw his father becoming more cold and more severe with every passing day. He knew that Don Juan, like the complaining colonists, had spent his entire fortune. Any new expenses had to be paid by their relatives in Mexico. He knew, too, how hard his father had tried to discover everything of value in the new land. The only result was that many of the people had turned against him. Cristóbal could see his father growing more and more desperate as the months passed without any news. The boy may have wondered whether his father had done wrong in ordering the executions of the captains, but those were the days when generals and people in authority had the power of life and death over their followers. Besides, the fierce family pride of the high-born Spaniard probably made it impossible for him to admit that his father could make a mistake.

One warm day in September, a soldier galloped into the plaza shouting that a group of men was coming up the valley. The word flew like a shower of sparks from house to house. The relief expedition! Word from New Spain! Soon all the people were spilling from the houses into the plaza, frantically eager to hear the news.

Don Juan felt his heart sink as he saw the small force marching up the bank to the pueblo. There were only eight men, seven soldiers and a priest. Behind them came a few pack mules and extra horses. The captain in charge leaped from his horse to salute Don Juan and hand him a packet of letters. As the man spoke, the lines of the governor's face relaxed. This was only the advance guard. A relief expedition was coming from Mexico with food and supplies for the colonists and reinforcements for the army. They would arrive in due time.

The governor's deep-set eyes were glowing as he turned to explain to the waiting colonists. The viceroy had approved his requests. His captains were busy recruiting men in Mexico. This was the best news that had come to the colony for a long time.

The waiting began again, but this time it was different. Knowing that he would have troops enough for further exploration, the governor could make plans for the future. He spent long hours questioning Jusepe about Quivira and discussing with his officers another attempt to reach the South Sea. A new optimism seemed to sweep the camp, too. Since new supplies were on the way, people could endure their broken shoes and ragged clothing for a while longer. Even the endless corn and beans they ate seemed less monotonous because they looked forward to the food and wine that would come with the supply train.

The relief expedition reached San Gabriel, the new capital to which the Spaniards had moved, on Christmas Eve of 1600. Almost two years had passed since Don Juan sent his captains to Mexico! The weather was bitterly cold. Snow lay deep in the valley. The Río Grande was frozen over in places, so that men rode across it on horseback. The newcomers with the expedition, accustomed to the mild climate of Mexico, had suffered greatly from the cold. However, their reception when they reached the capital warmed them through and through.

The colonists were wild with joy. They cheered

for Captain Villagrá as they had when he left. They wept and embraced the other captains and soldiers who were returning. They welcomed with embraces, also, the new recruits to the colony. And all the while, their eyes kept turning to the long, long pack train bringing the food and supplies they needed so badly. Soon the newcomers had joined the colonists around the fires of smoky cottonwood logs in their quarters and plans were under way for a feast to celebrate their arrival. This was a real Christmas!

Perhaps the happiest boy in the capital that Christmas was Cristóbal. Securely sealed amid the mass of cargo brought by the train was a box marked "Don Cristóbal." Inside were many things to delight the heart of a fourteen-year-old boy of his day. There was fine material for making a new suit, a beautiful brown hat trimmed with gold braid and pearls, and even a bag containing 800 cakes of soap! But the gifts that pleased him most were a complete set of handsome trappings for his horse and a gilded sword and dagger to wear in his belt. Cristóbal probably fingered the fine material and thought it would have been better to receive something stronger to wear in this rough land. But he was happy, anyway, as any boy would be with such wonderful gifts.

At the welcoming feast for the new colonists and soldiers, Don Juan made a speech, as usual. He reviewed the explorations made by his army up to the present time. He ended by saying that, thanks to their presence and to the generosity of the viceroy, he expected to continue his explorations. He promised that during the next spring another expedition would set out, either for Quivira or for the South Sea.

ADVENTURE IN QUIVIRA

Quivira! That was the magic word in the New Mexican capital in the spring of 1601. The men of the army had voted in council meeting to explore Quivira before the South Sea. Perhaps it was because Quivira was thought to be much closer. Or perhaps it was because of the stories of Jusepe. He had talked a great deal about a settlement he had seen, which he estimated to be over fifteen miles long and four miles wide. He had also heard of larger settlements with great wealth farther on. The dream of golden cities again warmed the Spaniards' hearts as they made their preparations during the spring months.

The governor must have studied his situation carefully during those months. He knew that the discontent in the colony made his absence dangerous. He also knew that one rich discovery would change every unhappy colonist into a devoted follower. Besides, His Majesty Philip III, now King of Spain, would expect him to explore the northern country to try to find the North Sea and the Strait of Anián.

Don Juan believed he was leaving the colony in safe hands. His lieutenant-governor, Captain Francisco de Sosa, was one of the wealthiest and most influential men of the colony. He had brought the wagon train safely to San Juan. His wife had organized the women of the capital to fight off the expected Indian attack. Such a family should be able to control any discontented settlers. To make assurance doubly sure, Don Juan tried to give his lieutenant-governor the support of men upon whom he could depend. The governor went personally to several friends, asking them to help look after the colony while he was away.

About eighty officers and soldiers, accompanied by two priests and Jusepe as interpreter, left the capital in late June, 1601. Behind them came a long train with seven hundred extra animals and several carts loaded with provisions. Led by the general, with Cristóbal and Vicente at his side, the expedition moved down the Río Grande and then east through a pass in the wall of mountains. Past the pueblo of Pecos they went and on to the Canadian River. They followed the Canadian a long way, even after it plunged off the Rocky Mountain Plateau down to the Great Plains. Here they began to see occasional teepee villages of the Plains Indians. Jusepe reminded the Spaniards that the presence of these Indians meant that the buffalo herds were near by.

Then, one day, there they were! The first sight of those lumbering animals must have been a great thrill for Cristóbal, after all the stories Vicente had told him. To make it even more exciting, he saw something that even Vicente had not seen before. Not far away, a single white spot showed in the brown mass of the herd. It was something quite rare—a white bull! Everyone told Cristóbal that it was a sign of good luck.

They were still following the Canadian when it entered a band of dunes where the horses sank over their hocks in the sand, and the cart wheels refused to move. There they turned north. After traveling several days through pleasant country, they came upon a large Indian encampment. It contained five or six thousand people. They wore little clothing and painted their bodies and faces with black and red stripes. They came to meet the Spaniards, raising their palms to the sun and then touching them to their chests. They probably belonged to the tribe which we now call the Kansa Indians.

With the help of Jusepe, Don Juan inquired about the country ahead. One man squatted in the dust and made a circle with grains of corn. Partly by signs and partly by gutteral words that Jusepe understood, the chief explained that this circle represented his village. A much larger circle was made for the tribe beyond this one. Those people, the chief said, were his enemies. He added excitedly that they were the ones who had destroyed the last Spanish expedition, the one with which Jusepe had come. They had set fire to the grass and burned them to death. Thinking that Don Juan's army had come to punish his enemies, the chief offered to guide the visitors to the other tribe. About one hundred of the Kansas marched with the Spaniards until late the next day, when they reached a wide river. The chief announced that his men would camp there while the white men went forward to meet the enemy.

The next morning, Don Juan's men forded the river and set off in the direction pointed out by the Kansa chief. Their way led across a pleasant countryside where small streams flowed between rolling hills. Late in the afternoon of the second day, the scouts rode back to report that an army of Indians was gathering on a hill ahead. The entire slope was prickly with feather headdresses and spears. As they watched, a large force of Indians came charging down the hill, shouting and brandishing their spears. As they ran, they scooped up handfuls of dirt which they tossed into the air as a sign of war.

Don Juan did not want to fight. His only desire was to explore the land that lay beyond. He ordered his men not to use their weapons unless it was necessary. Instead, they were to raise their palms to the sun, as the Indians did, to show they came in peace.

Seeing this sign made by the newcomers, the Indians, too, halted. Their leaders seemed to be talking over the situation. Then a man wearing a tall feather in his hair came forward with a small group of warriors. The general and his chief officers dismounted and went to meet them. These Indians, who later were called the Wichitas, had a strange, owlish appearance due to a stripe painted from their ears to their eyes. The chief removed a necklace of animal teeth and small bones from his neck. Approaching Don Juan, he indicated that he wanted to give it to his new friend. The general bowed his head and the Indian placed the ornament around his neck. The bones clanked with a dull sound against the metal breast plate.

As pleased as children with their new friends, the Wichitas invited the newcomers to visit their settlement, a short distance away. Don Juan cast a cautious eye at the sun, low in the west, and answered that they would make the visit the next day.

While the soldiers set up tents and started cooking

fires, the Indians visited the camp with gifts. They brought ears of corn and huge round loaves of corn bread. One Spaniard wrote that they were "as big as shields and two or three inches thick."

The next morning, the Wichita chief, who was called Catarax, appeared with five of his warriors to escort the visitors to their village. Hardly had they arrived when shouts and war whoops sounded from the rear. Across the meadow behind the camp came a large number of Kansa warriors who had followed the Spaniards. Spies must have reported that the newcomers had made friends with his enemies, for the Kansa chief was angry. He told Don Juan that Chief Catarax was trying to lure him into a trap, where he would be destroyed as the previous expedition had been.

Don Juan and his officers looked soberly at one another. Perhaps the man was right. Perhaps this explained the sudden friendliness of the Wichitas. Perhaps this was the reason for the invitation to visit their village. There was only one thing to do, they decided. They must take Catarax and his warriors prisoners and make the chief a hostage for the safety of the Spanish force. Don Juan ordered that the Indians were to be treated kindly. Catarax had aroused much respect among the Spaniards.

Chief Catarax accepted his captivity with dignity.

He explained to his warriors that they would not be harmed if the visitors were not molested. He made the same explanation to his people as he met them on the way to the village. So the small Spanish force met with no resistance. When they reached the settlement, however, they found it deserted.

Disappointment dulled the eyes of the Spanish soldiers as they entered the Wichita village. So this was the famous Quivira they had come so far to see! It was a large town, about twelve hundred houses, according to their estimate. The houses were small, round buildings, thatched with grass from roof to ground. Each one had a small platform or terrace near the top. Ladders for reaching the platforms stood against the walls of the houses. Curious soldiers climbed to some of them where they found ears of corn drying in the sun. From that height, too, the cornfields and gardens surrounding the village could be seen.

After a thorough search had unearthed nothing more valuable than a good supply of corn and some necklaces of animal bones, Don Juan, Vicente, and Jusepe held a conference with Chief Catarax. They questioned the chief about the region beyond. Were there many people? Were their houses like those of the Wichitas, or were they made of wood or stone? The chief answered that there were many people in settlements even larger than this one, but that they all lived in the same kind of houses. He then warned his captors against continuing their march. His own people who had left the village, he said, were already warning the settlements ahead. The result would be that the small Spanish army would meet a force so great that not even its famous "firesticks" and horses could save it. It would be swallowed up and destroyed.

Don Juan drew himself up stiffly. He thanked Catarax for the information, but said that the Spaniards would go on. The soldiers looked at one another in dismay. Judging from the large numbers of Indians they had seen in recent days, the words of the chief could well be true.

That night Catarax and his warriors slipped away from the men who were guarding them. They probably went to join the gathering Indian army, the soldiers grumbled. As they marched on next day, they passed other villages of grass lodges. All of them were deserted. Soldiers and officers watched the horizon uneasily.

In camp that night, the men presented General de Oñate with a petition asking him to turn back and giving their reasons for the request. Few really thought that the stern old general would bow to the wishes of his men, but he did. The next morning, the army began its return journey. Three days later, they were crossing the hilly country toward the Kansa camp. Confident in the friendliness of the Indians, they had left the armor off their horses. Vicente and a dozen men were riding ahead as scouts, more because it was customary than because they expected any trouble.

Suddenly someone shouted and pointed ahead. The scouts were racing toward them at full speed! The army halted. As the scouts drew near, the waiting soldiers gasped at the sight of an arrow which had pierced the upper part of the neck of Vicente's horse. A long, red furrow along the flank of another animal showed where an arrow had creased the flesh.

Vicente sprang from the horse and threw the reins to a servant. Then he reported to Don Juan. He and his scouts had ridden up to the Kansa village as friends. But the warriors who came out were not friendly. They were armed and had tried to surround the scouts. Vicente and his men whirled their horses in immediate flight. Even so, two of the horses were wounded. The Spanish soldiers looked at one another in amazement. Why had these Indians changed from friends to enemies so quickly? The only explanation seemed to be that the Kansas were angry because the Spaniards had not attacked the Wichitas.

General de Oñate set his jaw. He had made every

effort possible to avoid fighting the Indians on this
journey. He would still keep trying. He ordered his
men to put the armor on their horses, load their guns,
and ride in close formation. When they approached
the settlement, they were to lift their hands in the
sign of peace. Only when he gave the order were they
to use their weapons.

Cristóbal's heart must have been thudding with
excitement as he rode forward with the rest. This was
the first time he had ever seen battle action. He
lifted his palms with the others as they approached
the warriors drawn up across the path. The answer
was a shower of arrows. The line of Indians, each
with a leather shield that covered his entire body,
stretched into a semicircle that threatened to enclose
the unwelcome visitors. The Spanish army of less
than one hundred men was faced by a force at least
five times that many.

Don Juan shouted an order to fire. His voice was
drowned in a mighty war whoop as the Indians released another shower of arrows. Stones and flint-
tipped war clubs, too, came hurtling toward the Spaniards. Crash! The harquebuses roared and spat flame.
Swords flashed as the soldiers charged. Cristóbal
snatched his blade from its sheath and charged with
the rest. He did not use his sword, for the Indians
fled to the shelter of a rocky hill nearby. But he felt

a great thrill as he rode with the soldiers. Now, at last, he was grown up!

Though the Indians had retreated for the moment, the battle was far from over. They were driven back time after time to the shelter of the hill. Each time fresh warriors came screaming out to send a hail of arrows against the Spaniards. Their armor saved the Spanish soldiers serious wounds, but many of them were struck by arrows.

Seeing so many of his men wounded, Don Juan ordered a retreat. To the surprise of the Spaniards, the Indians did not pursue them. Perhaps it was because they had lost a large number of men before the gunfire of the Spaniards. In their well-guarded camp that night, the men rested and had their wounds dressed. Even though most of them had been struck, the limping little army started back to New Mexico the next day.

It was late November when it approached the capital. Snow had fallen in the valley. It had melted underfoot, and the trails were slippery. Snow still clung to the north slopes of nearby hills and to the bark on the north side of the trees in the valley. The men shivered under the cold steel of their armor. When a bend in the river brought the capital into view, everyone broke into a cheer.

Soon, however, they were looking questioningly

at one another. There seemed to be no movement about the pueblo. Where was everybody? They had reached the clearing around the pueblo when the lieutenant-governor appeared in one of the entrances. Seeing the approaching force, he came forward at once to greet them. He must have called to others inside, for several men came hurrying out.

Don Francisco greeted the general and the officers with an embrace. His gray-bearded face looked worn and tired and a little frightened.

Then, as befitted the bearer of bad news, he bowed his head and told Don Juan why the settlement was so quiet. Most of the colonists had deserted and returned to New Spain!

JOURNEY TO THE SOUTH SEA

The face of Don Juan looked as if it were chiseled from gray granite when he heard the news. Everything he had done seemed to be in vain. His long, hard exploring trips had discovered no wealth in the new land. All his efforts to hold the colony together had failed. Over two-thirds of the colonists had deserted, leaving behind only twenty-six loyal men. Adding these to the fighting men back from Quivira, he would have an army of a little over one hundred men—not enough for continuing the exploration and guarding the capital at the same time.

But that was not all. The reports the deserters would carry to Mexico might cause the king to call back the rest of the colonists. Don Juan knew perfectly well what those reports would be like. Just as he himself had exaggerated the good things about the country in his reports to keep the king interested, the deserters would exaggerate the bad features to justify their leaving. Every mistake their governor had made would be painted as a crime. People who had used the food and blankets taken from the Indians would denounce the governor for sending soldiers to collect those things. His deep-set eyes were bitter as he stared at the quiet pueblo.

But Don Juan was not a quitter. Tired as he was, he immediately set up a court to try the absent colonists. They were judged guilty of treason for deserting an expedition sent out by His Majesty the king. Some of his council thought that it still might be possible to overtake the fugitives. Although they had been gone for about two months, they would have to travel slowly with their carts and all the animals they had taken. Vicente was ordered to lead a picked group of men to try to bring them back. If this was not possible, he was to proceed to Mexico City to talk with the viceroy. He was to ask that three hundred more soldiers be sent at royal expense. Don Juan offered to pay for still another hundred, even though he would have to ask his relatives to bear the cost. With four hundred fresh soldiers added to those he had, the general was sure he could complete the explorations that still waited.

A detail of worn, tired men joined the field commander to set forth on this mission. Shivering in the raw, winter wind, they drew thin, worn cloaks over their rusty armor. Vicente's face showed lines of pain, for he was still suffering from wounds he had received in a southern pueblo before he went to Quivira. Even the horses looked tired, though they were the best and freshest the camp could provide.

Governor de Oñate and Cristóbal, with the three priests and the remaining colonists, were there to see them off. Everybody stood silently in the cold wind until the small procession was lost around the bend in the river. Then they hurried back to the cottonwood fires in their quarters. Don Juan sat down heavily at the rough table that served him as a desk. Once again, there was nothing to do but wait.

He had to wait only a few weeks, however, to learn that he would not get his colonists back. Messengers sent by Vicente reported that the deserters had reached Santa Barbara in New Spain before they could be overtaken. The viceroy had ordered them to stay there until he could investigate the matter. Following Don Juan's order, Vicente was going on to Mexico City. If the viceroy refused to send more men, Vicente would go to Spain to lay the matter directly before the king.

Waiting began then in earnest. Almost a year had passed when news came that Vicente had gone on to Spain. Don Juan knew then that the viceroy had refused his request. He continued to wait, while winter passed, and spring woke the leaves again.

In May of 1603, a group of four new priests arrived, escorted by a small squad of soldiers. The viceroy had sent the four to care for the Christian Indians after he had learned that most of the priests who had come with the colony had left with the deserters. The new arrivals brought some news, none of it good. The viceroy was still investigating the accounts of the colonists who had returned. Black stories were circulating in Mexico about conditions in the New Mexico colony. The priests looked at the pleasant valley and the Spanish flag flying above the adobe buildings as if they were surprised at what they saw.

Late in 1603, Vicente returned to New Mexico. He arrived with a train of pack mules carrying new military supplies—helmets, swords, coats of arms, harquebuses, buckskin jackets. He also brought news —bad news. The king and the Council of the Indies refused to send back the colonists who had deserted or replace them with new men. All decisions on these matters were to be left to the viceroy. Vicente had to confess to his uncle, too, that there was much discussion, both in Mexico and in Spain, about whether the colony was worth the money it had cost.

Don Juan felt that there was only one more chance

to get the wealth that would make the colony a success. That was to find the pearls that were said to exist in the South Sea. He must have thought about it long and carefully. He could not afford to strip the capital of the soldiers needed to defend it. However, if he took only twenty-five or thirty men, there would be enough left. The colonists living there now were much more dependable and loyal than the former group. With Vicente as their acting governor, they should be all right.

So in October of 1604, General de Oñate led a group of thirty men westward, as he had done just six years before. Cristóbal was with him, of course, and two priests, Father Escobar and Brother San Buenaventura. The flags fluttered as bravely and the sun sparkled as brightly on the ridged helmets as it had in 1598. But now the spirit of the men was different. Then they had looked forward eagerly, expecting to see a golden city at every turn of the trail. Then they had believed that the mines Captain Farfán had found would make the colony rich. Now, they expected no golden cities. They hoped that the stories of pearls in the South Sea were true, but they were not sure.

On they went across rough country, cut by dry gullies. They passed Acoma without stopping. They could see newly built houses on the cliff, for many

Acomans had escaped from their masters and returned to their old home. They stopped only a short
time in friendly Zuñi and then went on to the Hopi
country. They would follow the trail blazed by Captain Farfán to the mines. After that, Don Juan was
determined somehow to find the South Sea.

The way led over mountains and streams and
through wide pine forests. Rabbits, wild sheep, and
deer bounded up the slopes. About the middle of
November, they found the stones Captain Farfán and
his men had heaped up to mark the mining claims
they had staked out. The small army did not linger
at the mines, however, for the South Sea was their
goal this time. On they marched to the west, searching for a large river the Indians had told them would
lead them to the sea. They reached that stream, now
called the Colorado, in December. In spite of the
fact that it was winter, they found the weather
pleasant, and it grew warmer as they went south.

Several tribes of Indians lived in the valley of the
Colorado. Their settlements of brush-covered huts
sometimes extended for miles. Naked men and children swarmed out of these houses to see the strange
visitors. The women, who wore short skirts made of
strips of bark, were more shy, but soon they also
joined the crowds. Curiously, they touched the
armor, fingered the leather of boots and saddles, and

stared at the horses. Generously, they shared their scanty food supply of corn, beans, squashes, and wild seeds. The horses were not so lucky. There was little grass for them and not enough corn for both animals and humans.

One day the Spaniards decided to find out whether the Indians knew of any metals in the region. Approaching a group of men, Don Juan showed them some silver buttons and a spoon and asked them if they had ever seen metal like this. The Indians examined the objects gravely, passing them from hand to hand. Then the chief, Otata, looked up and nodded, pointing toward the west. Another man made the sign for a day's journey and held up five fingers. The Spaniards looked at one another, hardly daring to believe their ears and eyes. Cristóbal went running for a silver plate from his father's camping equipment. The Indians bent over it. One man took it and tapped it with his knuckles. It made the same sound, he said, as some cooking vessels used by a tribe which lived west of the valley. The Spaniards crowded around eagerly. Where was this place? Had they ever gone there? The Indians said they had. The metal was dug from a mountain across a stretch of water. One man drew a map in the dust. Another sketched a canoe to show how they crossed the water.

Excitedly, the visitors showed their hosts articles

of brass and small golden ornaments. Father Escobar
even brought out his cherished brass watch. Again,
the Indians nodded recognition. Beside a lake nine
or ten days' travel away, there were people who wore
bands of this metal on their wrists and arms, they
said. Though the Spaniards found their hearts pounding with excitement, they were still doubtful. Was it
possible? Could this journey end in a golden city?

Don Juan asked Chief Otata about Indian tribes
in the western region. The chief seized a stick and
started drawing a map on the ground. Don Juan
sent a man scurrying for paper so that the map
could be preserved. Scorning the feather pen and the
ink which was offered him, Otata took a charred
stick from a cooking fire and used it to draw his
map. As he showed the location of each nation, he
talked about the people who lived there. Here, he
said, lived a tribe with ears so long they dragged
on the ground and wide enough to cover five or six
people. Next to this nation was another who always
slept in trees. The Spaniards were bursting with
questions. Why did they sleep that way? Were there
dangerous animals or reptiles in the region? Otata
did not seem to understand. He went on with his
sketching. Here was a lake, he said. The people who
lived on its banks slept under the water. Cristóbal
looked doubtfully at the man. One of the soldiers

burst out with an exclamation. That was not possible! Two or three of the Indians nodded solemnly. One man said that he knew the people of that region. It was true. The stories went on. Those Indians were having fun with the Spaniards, as many tribes still do with tourists who visit their reservations.

The Spaniards continued down the valley through many friendly villages. Farther and farther south they went. One day a scout came riding wildly up to the general, shouting that he had seen the sea. The entire company raced to the hill where the scout had stood. There, sparkling in the distance, were the waters of what we now call the Gulf of California. The men yelled with joy. They thumped and pummeled one another. To show their delight, they made their tired horses rear and prance.

When they reached the place where the Colorado empties into the gulf, they were overjoyed with what they found. This place would make a splendid harbor, they said, capable of sheltering a thousand ships. The descriptions given by the Indians made them think that the peninsula of Lower California was an island. For that reason, they thought the harbor was on the ocean they called the South Sea. Such a port would be very important for trade with New Spain and the Far East.

General de Oñate halted his happy company on

the shore. He and Brother San Buenaventura waded out into the water. Don Juan was resplendent in freshly polished armor, with his shield on one arm and his sword in hand. The Father wore the simple brown robe and sandals of the Franciscans, but he carried a beautiful cross of hammered silver. The rippling water washed around the general's boots and the hem of the priest's habit. Higher and higher it rose. When the water reached his waist, Don Juan raised his arm and struck the surface with the flat of his sword. In a loud, clear voice, he announced, "I take possession of this sea and harbor and all the shores washed by this sea in the name of the king of Spain, our lord." The priest, holding the crucifix high, also proclaimed possession in the name of God and the holy church.

A lone trumpet blared, and the harquebuses fired a salute. As the smoke drifted out across the quiet water, the general and the priest waded back to shore. The soldiers were shouting themselves hoarse. Their dream was realized. They had reached the South Sea!

After the ceremony, the army visited Indian settlements along the coast. Here they found many oyster shells used for ornaments. The general traded for a number of them. Then he showed the people white beads and asked if they ever found such beads in the shells. When they said they had, Don Juan offered handfuls of the bright colored beads he carried to anyone who would bring him a single white bead from one of the shells. Not one appeared. The soldiers watched for pearls in necklaces and other Indian adornments. Not one was seen. It was the greatest disappointment of the journey.

At last, it was time to decide what they should do next. In open council, the men earnestly discussed their situation. Weighed against their eagerness to investigate the stories of gold and silver was the fact that their store of provisions was very low. Besides, their horses were exhausted by the long journey and the lack of pasture on the way. The poor animals were in no condition to set out on another unknown trail through country that seemed too barren for good grazing.

The decision to return to the colony was not really disappointing because everyone, from Don Juan on down, expected to return. Their expedition had made important discoveries—the fine port, the many Indian tribes ready to be taught the Christian religion, the new accounts of gold and silver. Certainly the viceroy would send all the men needed to explore this territory as soon as he received the report that Father Escobar was preparing.

The return journey was harder than the way out. It was so bad in the high, snowy mountains that they had to kill some of their horses for food. That meant they were in desperate straits, indeed. The Spaniards loved their horses and knew their great value in this rough land. What a relief it was to reach the friendly pueblos of Hopi and Zuñi! There both horses and men received the food needed to strengthen them for the last part of their journey.

About the middle of April they made camp at Inscription Rock. Most of the men had been here before. But when they left this time, there was something new on the rock, something you can still see if you go there. Carved on the sandstone cliff was the following inscription in Spanish: "Governor Juan de Oñate passed by here from the discovery of the South Sea on the 16th of April, 1605."

Nobody knows who carved that sentence on Inscription Rock over 365 years ago, but it may be that Cristóbal did it. The boy had very little education, for there were no schools in the early years of the colony. An official from New Spain wrote to the king on one occasion saying, "Don Cristóbal . . . is a youth . . . of whom it is said that he hardly knows how to read and write." This implies that, though he had less education than most sons of prominent families, he had some. We know that he signed his name as a witness to several of his father's reports. So it is possible that Cristóbal, now nineteen or twenty years old, was trying out his dagger on the soft sandstone as boys nowadays write or carve on walls and rocks. In this inscription, so rough that it looks like the work of an uneducated person, he may have found a way to express his pride in his father's achievements.

ĐON CRISTOBAL, GOVERNOR OF NEW MEXICO!

It was a hot August day in 1607 in the capital. The small rooms of the pueblo building were like ovens. The colonists could not bear to remain inside. While the children ran down to the river to splash in the cool water, the men and women gathered in groups in the shade of the house walls or under the big cottonwood trees. They talked restlessly, uneasily. Everyone knew that this day marked a turning point in the life of the New Mexico colony. Today, Don Juan de Oñate was writing a letter to the viceroy to resign his post as governor of New Mexico.

There were no secrets about the decision. Don Juan had talked it over with the town council. The men had reluctantly agreed that perhaps it was the best thing to do. They hoped that the king and the viceroy would send a governor wealthy enough to continue the explorations and develop the colony. Or, perhaps, these officials might be willing to supply men and money to a new leader. At any rate, the captains and soldiers were going to send a letter along with that of Don Juan reminding the rulers of the hardships suffered in the new land and asking for help.

Don Juan sat in his hot and stuffy quarters with the notary who was going to write the letter for him. The man was silent, his feather pen poised over a blank sheet of paper. Staring into space, the governor tried to arrange in his mind the things he should say. He thought about the many disappointments he had suffered on the expedition. Bitterest of all was the memory of the way his report on the discovery of the South Sea had been received by the viceroy. Father Escobar himself took the report to Mexico City, along with samples of coral, ores, shells, and stones. It was clear from the first that the viceroy had lost all interest in the new land. He said that, as far as he could see, Don Juan had found only "naked people, some pieces of inferior coral, and a handful of pebbles." As for the harbor they had found, he thought it would be too expensive to construct the docks and buildings necessary to make a sea port of the place. He was evidently very scornful of the stories heard from the Indians of the Colorado River valley, which Father Escobar had included in his report. Later the viceroy wrote to the king, "This conquest is becoming a fairy tale."

Even after he had learned what the viceroy had said, the governor did not immediately decide to resign. He waited, hoping that the king would read the accounts and order men and supplies sent to New Mexico. Now, over two years had passed since the report went to the viceroy. Even allowing a year for the news to travel from Mexico to Spain and a reply to come back, there had been plenty of time for the king to act. Don Juan realized at last that he would never receive enough help to finish his exploration to the North Sea or to follow to their sources those tantalizing hints about gold and golden cities. With a deep sigh, he came back to the present. He began to dictate his letter. The notary's pen marched like a soldier across the page.

Cristóbal, now a slender, handsome young man of twenty-two, came quietly to the door. He paused a moment, listening. Then he slipped away. He knew how it hurt his father to write that letter. The thought of leaving the colony hurt Cristóbal, too. In the first place, he thought his father had been unfairly treated. He should be given help to maintain the colony, instead of being practically forced to leave it. In the second place, the colony was home to Cristóbal. He had grown up here. He had been a child when he left Mexico. He would be a stranger when he returned. He felt homesick already as he looked at the outline of the mountains to the east.

After long months of waiting, the answer to Don Juan's letter reached the capital. It was brought by a priest, escorted on the dangerous journey by a detail of eight soldiers. As usual, everyone in the settlement rushed out to meet them. After the greetings were over, the priest handed the governor a packet of letters. Another packet bearing the royal seal went to a tall, black-bearded captain, Juan Martínez de Montoya, who received it with a look of surprise. Don Juan kissed his letters and held them above his head to show his loyalty to the king and the viceroy. Then he retired into his rooms with Cristóbal and Vicente.

With shaking fingers, he broke the seal and unfolded the stiff paper. Cristóbal saw him start with surprise. An angry flush reddened his face. In a choking voice, he told them what had happened. His resignation had been accepted, as he had expected. The thing he had not expected was that one of his own army captains had been appointed in his place. Juan Martínez de Montoya! Cristóbal remembered the captain's look of surprise as he took the packet with the royal seal. The newly appointed governor had arrived in New Mexico with the reinforcements on Christmas Eve, 1600. He was a tall, good-looking man and made friends easily with the colonists who were already there, especially with the leaders of the group which later deserted. He seemed to be fairly well-to-do, for he brought two complete coats of mail, four suits, sixteen shirts, ten horses, and many other things. But it was clear that he did not have the great wealth needed to continue the work Don Juan had been doing. Don Juan felt that he had been insulted by having an unknown and insignificant man put in his place. The colony had been insulted because no attention had been paid to the requests made by the captains and soldiers.

After the first shock was over, Don Juan called his servant. Soon the adobe walls were echoing with the sound of the trumpet, followed by the voice of the crier announcing a meeting of the town council.

The men of the colony were excited and restless when the governor entered the meeting. They were eager to know what the reply of the viceroy had been. Don Juan stood before them straight and erect, a Spanish gentleman from his frayed velvet doublet to the hand that rested on the hilt of his sword. On one side stood Cristóbal and Vicente. On the other side were Juan Martínez and two of his friends. The captain looked nervous and uncomfortable.

Don Juan spoke to the council, telling them that the viceroy had accepted his resignation. He had

called the council into session at this time, he added, to present the man appointed by the viceroy to take his place. Then he announced the name of the new governor. There was a moment of stunned silence. The men stared at the captain who had been chosen. Then they clamored to be allowed to speak. The viceroy had no right to appoint their officers without consulting the colony, one man said hotly. Others shouted agreement. They were free subjects of the Spanish Empire, said another. They should be able to choose their own leaders. At that, someone shouted that Don Juan de Oñate should continue to be the governor. The name of Don Juan was repeated all over the room. It was clear that most of the colonists wanted Don Juan to continue.

Don Juan's deep-set eyes glowed with pleasure. Nevertheless, he called firmly for order. The room was quiet as he explained that he was no longer acceptable to the viceroy. Though he appreciated the honor they had done him, he could not accept.

There was a moment of confused muttering. Then someone shouted Cristóbal's name. The young man gasped as if he had been splashed with cold water. The shout spread through the room. Cristóbal stared unbelievingly at the men there, older men, men whom he had admired and looked up to for years. Had they all gone crazy? He looked at his father for help. To his utter amazement, he saw that his father was smiling. With a sinking feeling in his stomach, mixed with a faint glow of pride, the boy realized that he, Cristóbal de Oñate, was being elected governor of the colony of New Mexico!

After the voting was over, Don Juan announced that he could see no objection to sending his son's name to Mexico as the colonists' choice for governor. Everyone could see that the old leader was pleased. The colonists who had stayed with him had shown their confidence in him and his family that afternoon. That knowledge must have helped to compensate for the desertion of six years before, as well as for the lack of support on the part of the viceroy.

As they left the room, Don Juan smilingly stood aside and motioned for his son to walk ahead of him. A flush darkened Cristóbal's face. He took his father's arm. Side by side, they walked out of the room.

So Cristóbal—Don Cristóbal, as we must now call him—came to be governor of New Mexico. He filled that post for more than a year while the viceroy, the king, and the Council of the Indies were deciding what to do with the colony. At first, Don Cristóbal found it hard to think of himself as the real governor. It seemed ridiculous for him to sign the instructions issued to the colonists or the reports that were sent to Mexico. After a while, however, he became accustomed to the new situation. He even got used to being greeted respectfully by the children as "Don Cristóbal" or "Mr. Governor."

The months of waiting for the viceroy's decision must have been pleasant ones for both Don Juan and Don Cristóbal. They knew they were surrounded by friends. There was no longer any need for exhausting expeditions in search of gold. There were not enough men for such journeys. Besides, no one really believed any longer that there was gold to be found. The colonists with their Indian helpers were planting more crops. Food became more plentiful and, as a result, they got along better with their Indian neighbors. It was a placid, peaceful period, with time to think back over the dreams and the achievements of the past.

In the meantime, life was not so peaceful in the city of Mexico. The viceroy and his advisers were shocked and displeased that the colonists had elected Cristóbal their governor. He was too young, they said. The viceroy wrote to the king, saying, "Don Cristóbal is very young, inexperienced, and of little wealth." Another official, as we have seen, repeated to King Philip the gossip that the new governor could hardly read and write.

Before the viceroy and the king could decide on

another governor, however, they had to decide whether there would be any colony to govern. Many of the advisers and the members of the Council of the Indies thought the New Mexico colony should be given up completely. It was too far away to be controlled, they said, and very expensive to maintain. If the colony were given up, however, there was the problem of what should be done with the Indians who had become Christians. Most people felt that it would be wrong to abandon them to become pagans again. Some thought they should be brought to Mexico where they could continue to be instructed by the priests. Others said that this would be wrong because it would break up the Indian families. Still others pointed out that most of the converts would run away rather than be taken to a strange land. The discussion went on for months and months. Many letters crossed the ocean between Mexico and Spain.

At last, the decision was made. The New Mexico colony would not be given up. It was to be maintained for two purposes: to hold the land which Spain claimed and to continue the spread of the Christian religion among the Indians. It would be placed under the special protection of the king, with all its expenses paid from the royal treasury. To make it less costly, it was to be kept small, and there would be no attempts to conquer more territory. The colony would consist of a governor and fifty soldier-settlers, with six priests and two lay brothers to work with the Indians.

A new governor was appointed for the colony. He was Don Pedro de Peralta of Mexico City. He was appointed in March, 1609, and was urged to set out for his new post as soon as possible. In April, a letter from the king to Don Juan ordered him to return to Mexico with Don Cristóbal within three months after he received the order.

So the day came when Don Juan and Don Cristóbal had to leave the little capital of New Mexico. A group of five or six soldiers went with them to protect them and their belongings on the road. There was not much property left to guard. Don Juan had brought twenty-six carts when the expedition marched into New Mexico. Just three were needed to carry the property of the two ex-governors back to Mexico. And instead of the herd of horses the general had brought, he returned with only the mounts necessary for the journey.

Every man, woman, and child in the settlement came to see their leaders off. Officers and soldiers, many of them fighting to hold back their tears, embraced the two. Women and childen wept openly. Many of these people had been with Don Juan for thirteen years, eleven in the settlement and two in

Mexico while they waited for the decision of the king. They had seen Cristóbal grow up. They felt as if they were losing a part of their own family.

Don Juan, who had grown old in the country, mounted his horse with difficulty. Cristóbal, blinking his eyes rapidly, swung easily onto his black mount. He was determined that the great-grandson of Cortés and the great-great-grandson of Montezuma would not weep. But the familiar lines of the pueblo building which had been home and the faces of old friends were blurred and misty as he gave the signal to start.

So Don Juan and Cristóbal left New Mexico. Behind them, they left something they had built, something into which they had poured their lives and their fortune. That was the first permanent colony settled by Europeans in what is now the United States of America. Founded nine years before the English Jamestown Colony and twenty-two years before Plymouth Colony, it was destined to play an important part in the development of the American West. Don Juan, in spite of his mistakes and the wrongs he was accused of committing, had done more to extend the Spanish Empire than any other man of his time. Even without golden cities, he had laid the wealth of vast lands, with all their promise, before the throne of His Majesty, the king of Spain.

biBliogRaphy

Amsden, Charles Avery. *Prehistoric Southwesterners from Basketmaker to Pueblo*. Los Angeles: Southwest Museum, 1949.

Bandelier, Adolph F., and Hewett, E. L. *Indians of the Rio Grande Valley*. Albuquerque: University of New Mexico Press, 1937.

Bolton, Herbert E. *Spanish Borderlands*, Chapter 6, "New Mexico." Chronicles of America Series. New Haven: Yale University Press, 1921.

————, Ed. *Spanish Exploration in the Southwest, 1542–1706*. Original Narratives of Early American History. New York: Barnes and Noble, Inc., 1946.

————. *Coronado on the Turquoise Trail*. Coronado Cuarto Centennial Publication, 1540–1940. Albuquerque: University of New Mexico Press, 1949.

Chapman, Charles Edward. *Colonial Hispanic America*. New York: Macmillan Company, 1933.

Cornish, Beatrice Quijada. "The Ancestry and Family of Don Juan de Oñate." In *The Pacific Ocean in History*, edited by H. Morse Stephens and H. E. Bolton. New York: Macmillan Company, 1917.

Goddard, Pliny E. *Indians of the Southwest*. New York: American Museum Press, 1931.

Gregg, Andrew K. *New Mexico: A Pictorial History*. Albuquerque: University of New Mexico Press, 1968.

Hammond, George P. *Don Juan de Oñate and the Founding of New Mexico*. Historical Society of New Mexico Publication in History, Vol. 2. Santa Fe: El Palacio Press, 1927.

Hewett, Edgar L. *Ancient Life in the American Southwest*. Indianapolis: Bobbs Merrill, 1930.

Lummis, Charles F. *The Spanish Pioneers*. Chicago: A. C. McClurg and Company, 1906.

Twitchell, Ralph E. *Leading Facts of New Mexico History*. 2 vols. Cedar Rapids: The Torch Press, 1911. Reprint. Albuquerque: Horn and Wallace, 1963.

Vestal Stanley. *The Old Santa Fe Trail*. New York: Houghton Mifflin, 1939.

Winship, George P. *The Journey of Francisco Vásquez de Coronado As Told by Pedro de Castañeda*. San Francisco: Grabhorn Press, 1933.

iNDEX